Cecil Sharp

Still Growing

English Traditional Songs and Singers
from the Cecil Sharp Collection

Compiled and edited by Steve Roud, Eddie Upton and Malcolm Taylor

Additional research by Bob and Jacqueline Patten

Preface by Shirley Collins

Introduction by Vic Gammon

Select Bibliography by David Atkinson

Published by The English Folk Dance & Song Society
in association with Folk South West

Published by the English Folk Dance & Song Society in association with Folk South West

EFDSS, Cecil Sharp House, 2 Regent's Park Road, London NW1 7AY, United Kingdom

British Library Cataloguing in Publication Data
Data available

ISBN 0 85418 187 3

3 5 7 9 10 8 6 4 2

Typeset in Minion by Rockford Graphics
Music set by Ros Clements and Eddie Upton
Publishing Consultants Nigel Lynn Publishing & Marketing Ltd
Printed in the United Kingdom
on acid-free paper by
Antony Rowe Ltd, Chippenham

CONTENTS

NOTES ON THE CONTRIBUTORS

David Atkinson is the author of *The English Traditional Ballad: Theory, Method, and Practice* (2002), and a member of the editorial board of *Folk Music Journal.*

Vic Gammon is Senior Lecturer in the School of Music at the University of Leeds. He is a member of the editorial boards of *Folk Music Journal* and *British Journal of Music Education.*

Bob & Jacqueline Patten live in Devon and have been researching West Country traditions since the late 1960s. The Patten Archive, comprising audio and video recordings, slides and photographs, and a library which contains many rare books, has become an extensive resource for arts projects, talks, articles and workshops, as well as general requests for information.

Steve Roud is the Local Studies Librarian for the London Borough of Croydon; the compiler of the Roud *Folk Song Index* and *Broadside Index* databases; co-author of the *Oxford Dictionary of English Folklore;* and a member of the editorial board of *Folk Music Journal.*

Malcolm Taylor has been librarian in charge of the Vaughan Williams Memorial Library for over twenty years and received an OBE in 2002 for services to music librarianship and heritage.

Eddie Upton is Director of Folk South West, the folk arts development agency for the South West of England. He has been singing traditional songs since 1964 and, since moving to Somerset in 1992, he has made a particular study of the songs collected by Cecil Sharp in the area.

ACKNOWLEDGEMENTS

The editors and other contributors to this book would like thank the following for their help and support:

Elaine Bradtke, Roly Brown, Paul Burgess, Keith Chandler, Ros Clements, Bill and Jude Crawford, George Frampton, John Francmanis, Peter Higginbotham, Felicity Greenland, Sam Richards, Derek Schofield, Sal, Brian and Simon Shuel of Collections, David Sutcliffe, Philippa Toulson, Andy Turner, Peta Webb.

And a very special thanks to Dave Bland, whose original research was the inspiration for this book.

Preface

It was on 22 August 1903 that Cecil Sharp heard his first 'living song' as he sat in the vicarage garden at Hambridge in Somerset, the home of his friend the Reverend Charles Marson. The gardener, John England, was singing quietly to himself as he worked, and the song was *The Seeds of Love*. Sharp rushed to fetch a notebook and pencil and wrote the song down. This fortunate chance altered the course of Sharp's life. Although he was already a member of the Folk-Song Society and thus aware of the work of other collectors, he'd never heard the songs sung other than as performances with piano arrangements in concert halls or drawing rooms. Realising the significance of what he'd just heard – 'a musical heritage of priceless worth' – he went on to collect over 500 songs in Somerset and North Devon during the next twelve months alone.

The more Sharp worked, the more urgent he felt the task was. In 1906 he wrote: 'There is so little time to be lost. The old singers are dying out rapidly and I shudder to think of the ruinous effects which a severe winter would have.' Although his own health was poor, his enthusiasm never waned, whatever life threw at him. He wrote to Anne Gilchrist in 1908: 'Am settling down again after a very disastrous holiday in my beloved Somerset. Two of the children went down with diphtheria, my wife had a near shave of typhoid … I managed somehow to collect a tremendous lot of songs, games, etc. But my mania for collecting is still unsatisfied – so I am working at the Marylebone Workhouse – 2000 inmates!'

Over the next few years, his collecting extended to Gloucestershire and Cornwall and other parts of the country. 'I sat one day from noon to 4 o'clock in a small lonely public house on the peat moors with a dozen cut-throats – at least they looked it – and I heard nothing but modal tunes the whole while!' Then in 1916, aware of the survival of British folk songs and ballads in the United States, he went to the Southern Appalachian states and there accrued one of the most important collections of folk music ever made, culminating in his posthumously published *English Folk Songs from the Southern Appalachians* (1932).

As one of his singers once said: 'I sometimes get an old line or refrain come into my head, and I think that's one of Granny's old songs, I wonder if Mr Sharp has that; but it goes so quickly, and I have no one now to jot it down, I forget the dear old ditties.' It was Cecil Sharp's vision and industry that saved these songs for us, noting down a remarkable 4,977 tunes in all. And it was his fervent hope that this music should become part of the national psyche, for, as he said: 'Is England, the land of Shakespeare, to go down to posterity as the only nation in Europe incapable of original musical expression?'

He is an Englishman who should be celebrated and to whom we should all be profoundly grateful.

Shirley Collins: Lewes, 2003

Cecil Sharp and English folk music

VIC GAMMON

Cecil Sharp is the most important folk song and folk dance collector that England ever produced. His achievements were, to quote Mike Yates, 'truly monumental'.[1] His collection of material is many times larger than any comparable English collection. He wrote the first important book on folk song. He popularised folk song and dance as recreational forms in the twentieth century. He created a national institution, since 1932 known as the English Folk Dance and Song Society. Perhaps most interestingly Sharp is still the subject of heated, sometimes vitriolic, debate and this is indicative of his influence and significance.

I want to emphasise a positive view of his achievement at the start of this essay because I am viewed in some quarters as a critic of Sharp. Through endeavour, determination, and enthusiasm he achieved a great deal in the field of folk song and folk dance collecting. This was done with scant resources, financial insecurity, and no small amount of personal suffering due to ill-health. I will return to the arguments over Sharp later, but it should be remembered he was no mean controversialist himself, and the debates we hear today have their origins in the supposedly genteel world of Edwardian England.

Cecil Sharp

Sharp was born in 1859 in Denmark Hill, South London (the year Darwin published *The Origin of Species*, Samuel Smiles *Self-Help*, and John Stewart Mill *On Liberty*, and John Brown was hanged following his leading of the Abolitionist raid on Harper's Ferry). He died in Hampstead in 1924 (the same year as Kafka, Puccini, and Lenin, and the first, ill-fated Labour ministry came to power under Ramsay MacDonald). His father, James Sharp, was a London slate merchant, and Sharp remained very close to him during his lifetime. Sharp senior had artistic inclinations and was sufficiently well off to retire from his profession before he was fifty. Sharp's mother, Jane Bloyd, the daughter of a City lead merchant from Wales, was a music lover and an able pianist. Theirs was a large family of eight children (four brothers and four sisters), Sharp being the third child and the eldest boy.

He was educated privately in Brighton and then at public school at Uppingham. He went on to study mathematics at Clare College,

Cambridge, in 1879. At Cambridge, Sharp seems to have devoted more time to his musical activities than to his mathematics and finished with an ordinary degree. Coming down from Cambridge in 1882 and probably at his father's behest, Sharp did what many young men of uncertain future did (or were pressured into doing) and went to one of the colonies, in this case Australia.

His years in Adelaide have been the subject of an interesting study by Hugh Anderson.[2] Anderson finds the account of Sharp's time in Australia in the biography by A. H. Fox Strangways and Maud Karpeles to be 'inaccurate, highly selective in its facts and subtly misrepresentative'.[3] Fox Strangways and Karpeles, he argues, did not attach much importance to Sharp's Australian years, other than to remark that the experience he gained stood him in good stead for the future and developed his social talents. Anderson, however, feels that it is 'probably true to say Cecil Sharp was an opportunist and social climber',[4] and points to the significance of the contacts he made in Australia for securing work in England after his permanent return. He certainly mixed with the social elite in Adelaide, often using his musical abilities as an entrée into colonial high society. It was also there that he met the outspoken Christian Socialist clergyman Charles Marson, who was later to prove an important link between Sharp and folk song. For most of his time in Australia Sharp worked in the public service, only turning professionally to music in his last few years, and then perhaps through force of circumstance. He returned to England for good in 1892, with the thought that he might return to Australia at some time.

Back in England, Sharp married Constance Birch in 1893. He had known her since before his departure for Australia, and she shared some of his artistic interests. He earned a living as a schoolteacher, firstly at Ludgrove in New Barnet (a preparatory school for Eton) and then, additionally, as principal of Hampstead Conservatoire, from 1895. Like many musicians, Sharp earned a living by combining different sources of income and part-time jobs – private music teaching, lecturing, conducting, directing amateur choral societies, and trying to get performances and achieve recognition as a Schumannesque composer. He eventually

Clare 2nd Boat Lent 1880. Sharp back row on the right.

became music tutor to the children of the royal family, and was from all accounts reputed a good teacher.[5]

I have long felt that Sharp's experience as a teacher was an enormously important aspect of his development, structuring the way he thought about the world and his ideas about what he should do with the material he was later to collect.

Discovering folk song and dance

There are iconic or mythic moments in Cecil Sharp's life. To call them iconic or mythic is not to imply that they never happened, but rather to say that in the retelling they have taken on a significance that they may not have had at the time. Thousands and thousands of people had seen morris dancing before Sharp did so at Headington on Boxing Day 1899, without its having been a life-changing experience for them. The following day Sharp notated five tunes from William Kimber, the team's concertina player. Later, Sharp was to say that that was the turning point in his life. But it is only in retrospect that the event takes on particular significance: his conversion to considering the collection and notation of dance as being of equal importance with his work as a song collector was a staged and relatively long-term process.[6]

The other important epiphany for Sharp was hearing Charles Marson's gardener, John England, sing 'The Seeds of Love' in the garden

William Kimber

of the vicarage at Hambridge in Somerset in August 1903. Fox Strangways' account of this event (which circulated widely in essentially the same form during Sharp's lifetime) describes the way in which, within the space of a day, Sharp discovered, notated, harmonised, and re-presented the song with piano accompaniment.[7] This was supposedly the trigger that projected Sharp and Marson into folk song collecting. However, the striking thing about the account (and I am not doubting that it has some truth) is the way in which it both encapsulates and prefigures the central activity that would engage Sharp over the next two decades.

One of the problems about a great deal of the writing on Sharp is the way in which he seems to be portrayed as a lone and heroic figure. The concentration on Sharp obscures the fact that he was part of a movement. He became the most significant and outstanding member of that movement, but his origins as a collector still lie in a current of thought, a sharing of sentiment, that ran through late Victorian society. The early signs of a genuine folk song movement in England can be identified in the 1880s, a dozen or more years before Sharp first collected a song. Within a few years and from dispersed parts of England there appeared collections of songs more or less faithfully gathered from oral tradition. The names of the collectors are well-known: Baring-Gould, Broadwood, Kidson, and Barrett. This initial activity seemed to falter a little in the 1890s, but the foundation of the Folk-Song Society in 1898 gave the small – and, I would argue, fragile – movement some sort of focus and institutional base.

Sharp was not a founder-member of the Folk-Song Society; he did not join until May 1901. The date is interesting. Clearly he was not in at the start, but equally his awareness of folk song predated by more than two years the encounter with John England in August 1903. The encounter could not have been so naive, so serendipitous, as the accounts make out. Marson, for example, writes that when Sharp heard the song: 'In a moment he recognised its value and we started a vigorous song hunt.'[8] As a member of the Folk-Song Society, he would have received its *Journal* complete with song variants and learned notes contributed by such

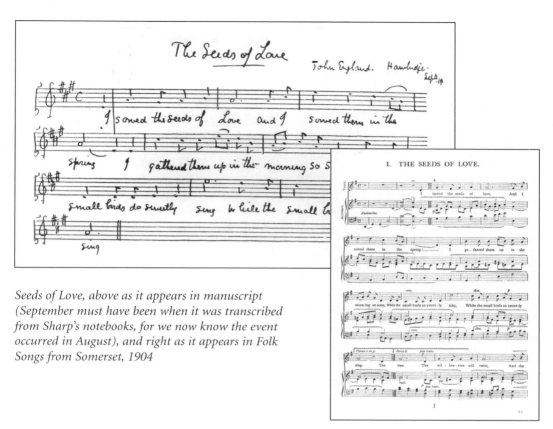

Seeds of Love, above as it appears in manuscript (September must have been when it was transcribed from Sharp's notebooks, for we now know the event occurred in August), and right as it appears in Folk Songs from Somerset, 1904

Marson family with John England (front, holding dog)

Charles Marson

people as Frank Kidson and Lucy Broadwood. He would have been exposed to some of the theorising on the subject. He had drawn on some folk song sources for his 1902 *Book of British Song for Home and School*. In that book, he commented on the work of previous folk song collectors: 'we have now, by the addition of this late but precious harvest to our garner, a collection of national song such as any nation might be proud of.'[9] He was a reader of the *Musical Times* and other periodicals that reported on folk song activities and publications. Above all, Sharp was a bright and intelligent man, notwithstanding his ordinary degree from Cambridge. My own feeling is that Sharp knew quite well what he was doing in that Somerset garden and had merely found the opportunity to do it. As with his involvement in the revival of folk dance, he recognised the potential of what others had started, carried it on, and by one method and another (not always admirable) outdid them. His energy cannot be doubted, and neither can his enthusiasm for the task. W. M. K. Warren, one of the Somerset clergymen who assisted him in his early collecting, wrote: 'What struck me most about Mr Sharp was his boundless enthusiasm for the preservation of what he recognised as a national

treasure and was in danger of being lost to the country for ever.'[10]

Sharp was very direct about his estimation of the early achievement of the Folk-Song Society. His sense of urgency about the task of collecting would brook no delay. The Society had only published 109 songs in six years; it had not met for two years and was moribund. There was, he argued, 'an immense amount of work to be done'. Sharp's impassioned outburst had an effect on the Society. The annual report for 1904 states blandly: 'Mr. Cecil Sharp, Principal of the Hampstead Conservatoire of Music, who has lately collected some hundreds of songs in Somersetshire and North Devon, joined our Committee.'[11] The decade following Sharp's commencement as an active collector – along with his friend Ralph Vaughan Williams, Percy Grainger, and those they inspired, including the great Scottish collector Gavin Greig – represents something of a golden age of folk song collecting. The movement, however, was already losing momentum before the First World War took the wind out of its sails. But Sharp was to demonstrate his resilience and determination. In America between 1916 and 1918, accompanied by Maud Karpeles, he made a rich collection of songs from the Southern Appalachian mountain region. Bertrand Bronson described this as being, in the American context, 'the foremost contribution to the study of British-American folk-song'.[12]

Sharp remained interested in folk song

Maud Karpeles and Cecil Sharp at Berea railway station, Kentucky, 1917

throughout his life, but during the first decade of the twentieth century dance increasingly occupied his consciousness and became a focus of much of his activity. Here the crucial influence was that of the social worker and feminist Mary Neal. In two brilliant articles Roy Judge has traced Sharp's development in relation to traditional dance. In the first of these, he shows how Sharp at first collaborated with Neal, then came into open conflict with her over questions of artistic standards and authority, and finally ousted her from the directorship of the Stratford-upon-Avon summer school and from her unofficial position of leadership in the folk dance revival itself.[13] The second article traces the way in which Sharp's interest shifted so that morris dance became the centre of his concerns and preoccupations. The crucial period here is 1906 to 1909. In 1906 his knowledge of morris dance was really quite limited and was 'a peripheral concern'. At this stage, he took more interest in the music than the dances themselves. By the end of 1909, by actively pursuing the subject in the field and by thinking about it, Sharp had developed real expertise in the morris dance as well as its music, and elaborated a whole set of ideas about its nature and function. His motivations for seeking to become an expert on this form of dance were no doubt twofold: first, a growing awareness of the potential of morris, and folk dance generally, as mass-participation revival forms; and second, the need to acquire power through knowledge in order to bolster his position in the growing rift with Mary Neal and their rivalry over the leadership of the folk dance revival.[14]

Sharp's relationship to the Folk-Song Society was always rather tense as a result of his criticisms and his unwillingness to conform to what might be described as a party line. In the case of folk dance, however, he simply outmanoeuvred the opposition and set up his own organisation in 1911 – the English Folk Dance Society. These two organisations came together, not without some difficulties, in 1932 as the English Folk Dance and Song Society.[15]

Sharp as collector

The evidence seems clear that Sharp was a talented collector of traditional material. We have to try to imagine ourselves back to that rather odd social encounter, the act of collecting folk songs. Contact with a singer may have been made through a local acquaintance of the collector. Often, a humble country person might get no more than a knock on the door, and be confronted by a stranger wanting them to sing old songs so that he or she could write them down. It is an encounter that is fraught with problems relating to differences of social background and gender, with a strong likelihood of things going wrong.

Mary Neal

Sharp collecting in Warwickshire, 1910

Sharp seemed to manage these situations very well indeed. As W. M. K. Warren wrote:

In his dealings with the old folk he exercised the most extraordinary tact and patience; it was only his undoubted love of these folksongs that overcame the suspicion of the singers. They had been accustomed to be laughed at by the younger generation for the pride that they took in what was called the old-fashioned song; naturally they were very chary of producing them if they thought that they were to form an entertainment; for they were to them their most treasured possession and were taken very seriously.[16]

As can be seen from some of the biographical sketches in this volume, some of Sharp's informants would speak very warmly of him.

No doubt, once over the initial shock, many people enjoyed the interest he took in them and their songs. In America, Olive Dame Campbell thought Sharp knew how to deal with country people: 'I found the singers very easy to handle,' he told her. Having studied Sharp's letters from his time collecting in the Appalachians, David E. Whisnant concludes that he 'was serious and industrious and uniformly gracious to and respectful of local people'.[17]

The other side of this coin is that in his obsessive search for traditional material one senses that Sharp was calculating as well as energetic, manipulative as well as affable. The giving of gifts or money (well documented in the sources), the ways in which he would lead singers on to give him songs, can be interpreted in different ways. On one level, as Sharp said to

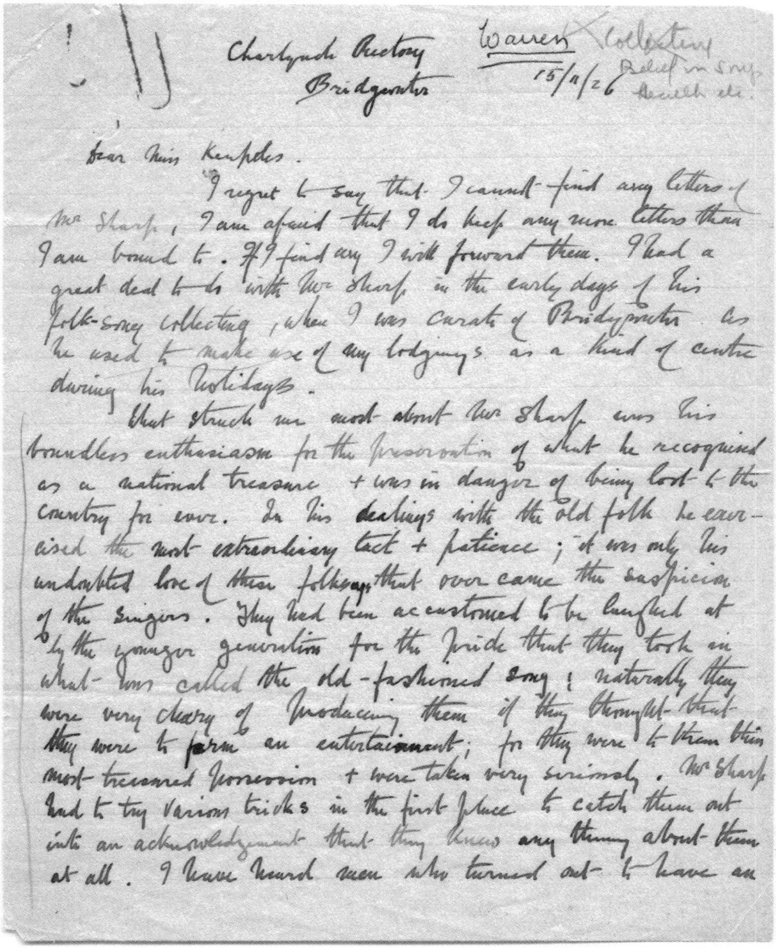

Louie Hooper, 'fair exchange is no robbery', but one doubts that it always was a fair exchange. On more than one occasion, Sharp writes about 'emptying' his informants. In pursuit of William Riley Shelton (known as Frizzly Bill or Singing Will), he wrote, 'Directly I have caught him and emptied him, I am going across the border into Tennessee …';[18] and of Mrs Carter of Beattyville, Kentucky, 'I have taken thirty songs off her already, and have not emptied her yet!'[19] I find this image disquieting because it suggests the material was much more important than the people were, but perhaps I am being oversensitive. There can be no doubt that Sharp took delight in the company of some of his informants and he must have communicated that feeling. He writes warmly in a number of places about happy hours spent talking and

listening to songs.[20]

Sharp's method of song collecting was a pencil and paper one. I have no doubt that he had an acute ear and as far as is humanly possible notated the songs with a high degree of accuracy. The 'humanly possible' qualification is important, for there is a lot of evidence that even the most accurate human ear is fallible and

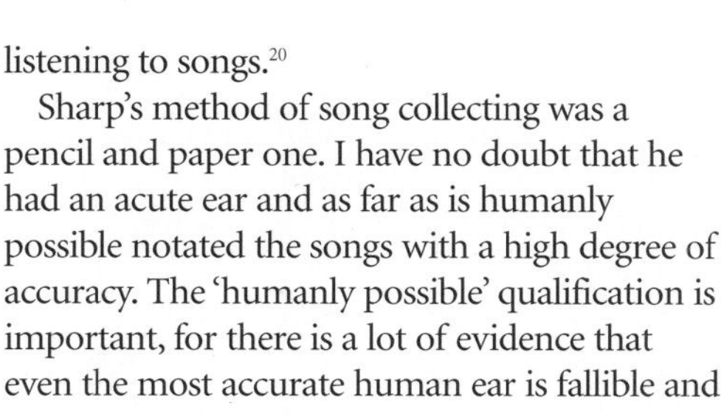

A CONCERT-LECTURE

ON THE

FOLK SONGS OF SOMERSET

WILL BE GIVEN

In S. Mary's Parish Hall,

WEDNESDAY, JANUARY 3rd, 1906.

Lecturer—CECIL J. SHARP.   Vocalist—MISS KAY.

TO COMMENCE AT **3** P.M.

TWO SHILLING TICKET.

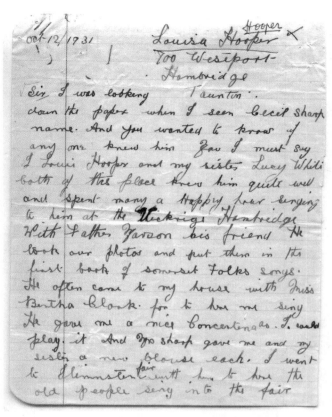

Page one of Louie Hooper's letter to Fox Strangways,
12 October 1931

and that therefore the recording might give a false impression of the usual performance. He argued that 'it is not an exact, scientifically accurate memorandum that is wanted, so much as a faithful artistic record of what is actually heard by the ordinary auditor'.[21] Sharp did make a few cylinder recordings, but generally he was happy to present a sort of 'idea type' of the tune, sometimes indicating melodic variations. One can sympathise with Sharp's points, but in taking this view, unlike Percy Grainger, he deprived later generations of the experience of hearing some of the singers who gave him songs. Thank goodness, we have Grainger's recordings of the wonderful Joseph Taylor. In addition, the BBC recorded Louie Hooper in 1942. A very few cylinder recordings of traditional performers made by Sharp do survive and are in the care of the National Sound Archive at the British Library.

E. C. Cawte has written an interesting study of Sharp's working methods in relation to the collection of sword dances and their associated songs in the north-east of England. By careful comparison of the archive and published material, he shows both the general accuracy of Sharp's accounts of the dances and the areas where he felt free to 'improve' on the material. In the published versions, indelicate song texts were suppressed (although this may have been at the behest of the publisher, and it is noteworthy that Sharp, true to his belief in 'scientific' collecting, did note them down). Cawte concludes that Sharp 'often preferred his own judgement to that of his informants in publishing dance tunes'.[22]

The collecting of songs involved making choices about which songs to collect. A considerable amount has been written about the processes of selection that took place during the act of collecting and afterwards in

well-trained musicians are liable to make mistakes. There is also a tendency to hear things in terms of pre-existing ideas and schemata that are already in the hearer's mind. An important part of Sharp's intellectual make-up was his belief in a 'scientific' method. Accuracy was important to him, but without actual sound recordings of the performances he notated it is difficult to be sure quite how precise his notation was.

The phonograph was the technological alternative, used by Percy Grainger in England and other researchers doing fieldwork in other countries – Béla Bartók in Eastern Europe and Frances Densmore among Native Americans in the USA, for example. It allowed, Grainger argued, a more considered, complete transcription of the performance. Sharp tried the phonograph but evidently felt more comfortable with his more impressionistic aural method. He thought that the phonograph made singers self-conscious and sometimes nervous,

Cecil Sharp using a favoured method of transport for his collecting trips

the processes of editing and publishing. All the collectors – and Sharp more than some – took from country singers those songs that conformed to the collectors' own notions of what constituted folk song. Sharp wrote his important 1907 book, *English Folk-Song: Some Conclusions*, precisely in order to define what was and what was not a folk song. All the evidence we have suggests that English country singers of the nineteenth and twentieth centuries sang an eclectic mix of songs. Of course, they sang what we think of as typical folk songs – 'The Seeds of Love', 'The Dark-Eyed Sailor', 'The Wraggle-Taggle Gypsies', and the like – and for this reason I find the idea of 'fakesong' unhelpful. However, in the case of Henry Burstow of Horsham (whose songs were collected by Lucy Broadwood and Vaughan Williams), Broadwood estimated that only about fifty or sixty of his songs – that is less than one-fifth – were 'of the traditional ballad type'.[23] Sharp did a great service in preserving examples of songs and song genres that otherwise would have perished and we owe him an enormous debt for that, but in considering what country people sang we should not mistake the part for the whole.

To understand what he did and why he did it, we need to look more closely into the complex of ideas that Sharp drew on, thought through, and articulated. I can do no more in the space available than give a sketch of what I consider to be some important aspects of Sharp's thought. I believe that his ideas and aspirations were a key motivating force behind the work he did. I want

to talk about three complexes of ideas, and to give them each a brief handle I will call them romantic nationalism, aesthetic Darwinism, and the idea of national regeneration.

Romantic nationalism

To Sharp a folk song was '… a song made and evolved by the people, as well as sung by them. The distinction is not academic; nor is it archaeological. It is intrinsic, for it distinguishes between two kinds of music that are fundamentally different from one another.'[24] The people may sing other songs, but unless 'made by the people' they were not folk songs. In another pithy statement, he wrote: 'If "traditional" means anything at all, it means that which has been handed down from generation to generation by word of mouth and not by printed or written document.'[25] Here is Sharp trying to make himself clear in a letter of 1922:

The word 'folk' has a very definite scientific meaning used as an affix to song, dance, lore and other products of the race that belong to primitive times and without this word I do not see how we are to distinguish between the art-product[s] that were the natural, instinctive human emanations from those that are the product of cultivated, sophisticated and conscious people.[26]

Sharp opposes the natural to the cultivated, the instinctive to the sophisticated and conscious.

In making these statements Sharp places himself firmly within, and draws on, a tradition of romantic thought that stretches back to the eighteenth century – to J. G. Herder, who could be said to have invented the term 'folk song' (*Volkslied*); to

Swalwell Sword Dancers

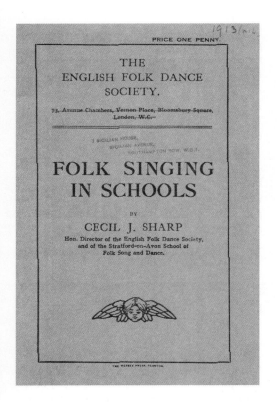

THE
ENGLISH FOLK DANCE
SOCIETY.

73, Avenue Chambers, Vernon Place, Bloomsbury Square,
London, W.C.—

7 SICILIAN HOUSE,
SICILIAN AVENUE,
SOUTHAMPTON ROW, W.C.1.

FOLK SINGING
IN SCHOOLS

BY

CECIL J. SHARP

Hon. Director of the English Folk Dance Society,
and of the Stratford-on-Avon School of
Folk Song and Dance.

PRICE ONE PENNY.

THE WESSEX PRESS, TAUNTON.

the brothers Grimm (whom Sharp both criticises and uses in his work); and to F. J. Child, the Harvard ballad scholar who held the ballads of oral tradition to be far superior to those 'contaminated' by print. Sharp's view is a version of what Jacob Grimm expressed as *Das Volk dichtet*, 'the people creates'.[27] These notions, deriving from the romantic movement, fuelled nineteenth-century interest in what became known (after 1846) as folklore – the collection and study of all sorts of traditional material, often obtained from poorer people in rural areas. Folklore collecting prefigures and in a sense gives the model for folk song collecting. Nineteenth-century folklore studies embodied two central ideas that were hugely influential. The *doctrine of survivals* sought to see the primitive within the civilised, the ancient within modern customary practices. The related *theory of origins* involved writers in a pursuit that was often very speculative and rarely definitive. Folklore defined a mode of thought that was highly influential and from which Sharp drank deeply.[28]

There is another aspect of romanticism

that Sharp picked up on (and I think this may have come via Wagner rather than directly from Herder). The German word *Volk* (the basis of the anglicised stem 'folk') can be translated as 'people' or 'race'. To Sharp, 'the earliest form of music, folk-song, is essentially a communal as well as a racial product. The natural musical idiom of a nation will, therefore, be found in its purest and most unadulterated form in its folk-music.'[29] In a pamphlet on *Folk Singing in Schools* (undated but ascribed to 1913) he wrote:

… folk-music has all the characteristics of fine art; that it is wholly free from the taint of manufacture, the canker of artificiality; that it is transparently pure and truthful, simple and direct in its utterance; and free from pretence and affectation, which are the invariable concomitants of bad art in general, and of bad music in particular.

A nation's folk-song is then: (1) the expression in musical idiom of racial ideals and aspirations; (2) the foundation upon which all the subsequent developments in music have been built; while (3) its intrinsic value – apart altogether from those special qualities which arise from its peculiar life-history, or its communal origin – is, within its own limits, as great as that of the finest examples of art-music.[30]

These appeals to nature and purity are very significant. Because it is unpolluted, the folk song somehow fights pollution. Such ideas as 'racial product', linked with ideas of purity, could and soon did have disastrous consequences. There is no doubt that Sharp is putting forward a racial theory: '… the songs are racial, *i.e.* they are couched in a musical idiom which must be the natural form of expression for the children of those who created it … [it will] be found simpler to teach children the music of their own country than that of any other'.[31] In his 1912 'Folk-Song Fallacy' debate with Ernest Newman in the pages of the *English Review*, Sharp seems to shift from ideas of race to nationality, but one doubts that there was a real shift in the nature of his thought.

The pamphlet on *Folk Singing in Schools* post-dated the exchanges with Newman and clings to the notion of race.

Such ideas of race could easily be manipulated in the sorts of ways that were witnessed in Italy and Germany in the 1920s and 1930s – yet, in many ways, they were common currency in late Victorian and Edwardian England (the Empire was built on them), although they were not usually given the particular direction Sharp gave them. England had long suffered from the gibe that it was 'the land without music', the accusation that the English were an unmusical people.[32] Like a significant number of musically interested people of his time, Sharp had a complex relationship with German music – awe mixed with jealousy, wonder with a sense of national inadequacy, and delight with feelings of inferiority. He was not the first to propose the idea that something should be done about English music in order to improve its quality and status, but he was part of a small, albeit vocal, minority in declaring so emphatically that a new national music should be founded on the basis of folk song: 'When every English child is, as a matter of course, made acquainted with the folk-songs of his own country, then, from whatever class the musician of the future may spring, he will speak in the national musical idiom.'[33] Sharp, who had performed and conducted a great deal of German music, thought that 'the present vogue of training English musicians to lisp in the tongue of the foreigner can have no beneficial outcome. It is, emphatically, not that way that salvation lies.'[34]

The tone of the pamphlet on *Folk Singing in Schools* is more firmly nationalistic:

Then, again, one of the first objects of education should be to arouse a spirit of patriotism in the children, to inspire them with a love of their country, with a just pride in the nation to which they belong. We in this country have suffered not a little from the cosmopolitan idea in education. It is not citizens of the world that we should strive to produce in the first instance – or, rather, if that is our ideal, we should realize that the first step

towards its attainment is the production of citizens distinctively national in type.
And that, I would observe, is what we cannot expect to produce if we bring up our children on German Kindergarten games, Swedish dances and foreign music. What we should do, of course, and what I believe every other European country does, is to see that our children in their earliest years are placed in possession of all those things which are the distinctive products of the nation to which they belong.[35]

It is interesting, perhaps ironic, to see the way Sharp uses German ideas to combat the dominance of German music in England. The combination of romanticism and nationalism was nothing new; it is a commonplace of nineteenth-century thought. In the context of England in the decades around the turn of the century, the idea of folk song as a basis for the creation of a national musical idiom was new. It was not exclusive to Sharp – but he did more about it than most people who thought in a similar way.

Aesthetic Darwinism

The model that Sharp proposed to explain the development of folk song derives from Darwinism. This is historically important, as it became the basis of an internationally agreed definition of folk song.[36] Sharp made no secret of this model, for he entitled Chapter 3 of *Some Conclusions* 'Evolution'.[37] He was not the first to try to apply Darwinism to music: Herbert Spencer, Hubert Parry, and others had tried it before him.

There is, however, one basic problem with trying to apply Darwinian ideas to social phenomena: Darwin's theory of evolution by natural selection deals with chance occurrences, random happenings, accidents in nature. In human society, the intervention of human culture and human agency, customary usages and the making of conscious choices, place human affairs in a different category from the laws of nature. In this respect, it is interesting that Sharp often used metaphors from nature in connection with folk songs – for example, comparing them to wild flowers. One can argue that it was necessary to do this in order to make evolutionary ideas applicable – for folk songs are not natural, they are products of human culture.

Here is an example of Sharp's take on Darwin:

Many, perhaps all of its [folk song's] most characteristic qualities, have subsequently been acquired during its journey down the ages, and represent the achievements of many generations of singers. Individual angles and irregularities have been gradually rubbed off and smoothed away by communal effort, just as the pebble on the sea shore is rounded and polished by the action of the waves. The suggestions, unconsciously made by the individual singer, have at every stage of the evolution of the folk-song been tested and weighed by the community, and accepted or rejected by their verdict. The life history of the folk-song has, therefore, been not only one of steady growth and development; there has also been a tendency always to approximate to a form, which shall be at once congenial to the taste of the community, and expressive of its feelings, aspirations, and ideals. It is clearly a case of evolution.[38]

Sharp goes on to suggest that this concept of evolution involves three principles: *continuity*, *variation*, and *selection*. *Continuity* is vouched for by the 'amazing accuracy of the memories of folk-singers' and counters the idea that oral tradition is a very inaccurate process.[39] Continuity links the past with the present and the future. I am convinced that some oral traditions do have considerable stability over long periods of time, but equally, in some conditions, oral traditions change rapidly or disappear altogether.

When Sharp considers *variation*, he gives a set of reasons for this widely observed aspect of traditional song. Some of his views seem reasonable enough, but I am not at all sure he is correct when he argues that the traditional singer 'is habitually unconscious of the tune that he is singing' and so 'any variation that he may introduce will be unconscious and unpremeditated also'.[40] I find this aspect of Sharp's explanation very unconvincing; it seems to be a version of the idea of the unschooled

illiterate. Sharp knows that traditional singers vary in skill. He writes that there are singers who 'display inventiveness of a high order' and names Mrs Overd and Henry Larcombe as examples.[41]

The most difficult aspect of Sharp's aesthetic Darwinism is that of *selection*. In the evolution of species in the plant and animal kingdoms, those variations will be preserved that are of advantage to their possessors in the competition for existence. However, in the evolution of folk tunes, as we have already seen, the corresponding principle of selection is the taste of the community. Those tune variations that appeal to the community will be perpetuated as against those that appeal to the individual alone.[42]

One of the important arguments in relation to Sharp's use of Darwinian ideas was put forward by Ernest Newman in his debate with Sharp in 1912. He asked, why should we assume that the passing of a song from person to person will improve it, when in fact its quality might deteriorate?[43] Such a view finds much support from the fragmentary nature of much collected song. Sharp's vision of a community selecting its folk songs, and so bringing about their evolution to a higher level of artistic beauty, might hold good for some ideal state of society, but it hardly works in the increasingly commercialised world of the late nineteenth and early twentieth centuries. Even so, the thought seems profoundly un-Darwinian. The evolutionary outcome for many species is oblivion. If we are to draw a Darwinian analogy, then the equivalent to a plant or animal species would be not an individual tune but rather, perhaps, a genre – for example, that which Sharp termed 'folk song' itself. Elsewhere in *Some Conclusions*, Sharp laments that folk song is dying. It is precisely because of selection by the community, because of its preference for other forms of musical expression – a social form of 'natural selection' or, rather, cultural selection – that folk song loses out. In the struggle for aesthetic survival, folk song bears a resemblance to the dodo, although perhaps it takes longer to die.

What, then, are we to make of Sharp's aesthetic Darwinism? Perhaps surprisingly, I think it has a lot going for it even if it is profoundly flawed. It is an attempt to theorise some interesting and complex issues. That Sharp does not get it quite right in a book written in a hurry almost a century ago does not invalidate the attempt – on the contrary, it gives us something to build on.

National regeneration

Sharp believed that folk song and dance could play a role in a form of national regeneration. This in turn relates to some of the themes I have discussed earlier. Sharp clearly felt that his collecting and dissemination work was of vital importance. Writing to Olive Dame Campbell in 1915, he said: 'I look upon it as a great privilege to have been able to do work of this kind, because … posterity will need the primitive songs and ballads to keep their two arts of music and dance real, sincere and pure.'[44] He maintained his dedication to collecting in spite of financial insecurity, and a 1917 letter from Maud Karpeles to Mrs Storrow reinforces this point: 'Really, the whole thing amounts to this – that he cannot do the collecting work and have the worry of earning a living at the same time. And, of course, there is no question but that he must go on with the collecting. That is the most important work for him to do, even though it meant that in doing it he would shorten his life by a few years.'[45]

Sharp actually came out with what seems like a social analysis of what he was doing, declaring publicly at Stratford-upon-Avon that he had but one aim: 'to ensure the transference of the songs and dances from one class to the other without hurt or harm'. He was heartily cheered for this.[46] He sincerely believed that the songs and dances carried some sort of regenerative power in themselves. Writing to an unnamed fellow collector he said:

I think it is very easy to be too touchy about the vulgarisation of things like folk-songs which one loves. A lover of Beethoven's music must feel the same if ever he thought of the way his favourite composer's music is being rendered in Crouch End, Hornsey, etc. If anything good is to be made popular, many things will happen which will shock the sensitive feelings of the elect. This is inevitable and must be accepted. I accept it in this case because I believe so sincerely in the innate beauty and purity of

folk-music that I am sure it cannot really be contaminated, but that it must and will always do good wherever it finds a resting-place.[47]

We can note the recurrence of the purity theme and the idea that folk music, of itself, will always do good. This is verging on the mystical or religious. It certainly indicates a belief in folk music having some sort of essence of effectiveness in itself, outside of human agency. *English Folk-Song: Some Conclusions* originated in a very heated debate over a Board of Education list of songs to be sung in schools. The final chapter is about the future of folk song and advocates the introduction of the singing of folk songs as a staple of school music:

If some such scheme as this, which we have been considering, were adopted in the State schools throughout the country, and in the preparatory schools of the upper and middle classes as well, not only would the musical taste of the nation be materially raised, but a beneficent and enduring effect would be produced upon the national character. For, good music purifies, just as bad music vulgarizes …

We may look, therefore, to the introduction of folk-songs in the elementary schools to effect an improvement in the musical taste of the people, and to refine and strengthen the national character. The study of the folk-song will also stimulate the growth of the feeling of patriotism.[48]

In the last sentence the ideas of national regeneration and romantic nationalism are brought together. The tone of the last chapter of *Some Conclusions* is almost messianic: 'Every week adds to the accumulation of the evidence in support of our contention that the re-introduction of folk-songs into England will effect many and notable reforms.'[49]

It would be easy to make light of Sharp's ideas about national regeneration, seeing them as naive and unduly optimistic. By a process of hard work, arguing, influencing, and cajoling, he did get traditional songs into the school curriculum. He became an Occasional Inspector for teacher-training institutions after the First World War and went around inspecting, giving demonstrations, and mostly complaining about what he saw and heard.

The notable reforms he hoped for never seemed to happen. The ultimate importance of his ideas is that they motivated his work. He really believed in what he did: no one should ever doubt his sincerity.

Cecil Sharp's legacy

As a great 'doer', Sharp has left us a large and complex legacy:

- his collection
- his publications
- his ideas and ways of understanding
- an influence on education
- the basis of a great national library
- an institution
- a national monument
- an ongoing debate about his work and his ideas.

Cecil Sharp's collection is a formidable one. It is many times greater than any other comparable collection. It is the real monument to his industry and dedication. The richness of the material is considerable, and it preserves some things that are unique. It is housed both at Clare College, Cambridge, and in the Vaughan Williams Memorial Library. It would be invaluable to have a proper critical edition of the collection, in the manner of the *Greig–Duncan Folk Song Collection*, but I doubt that I will see such a thing in my lifetime.

Sharp's publications continue to circulate, and people make use of them. They are a part of our culture, but (whatever his apologists say) they cannot be taken as a wholly accurate record. *Cecil Sharp's Collection of English Folk Songs*, edited by Maud Karpeles and published in 1974, was poorly edited, is selective, and while it gives an indication of the richness of the Sharp collection it remains less than totally reliable.[50] Karpeles, as Sharp's literary executrix, was also responsible for the promotion of his work and ideas in the time between his death and her own (in 1976). Indefatigable in her promotion of the Sharpian cause, she was responsible for new and revised editions both of *Some Conclusions* and of Fox Strangways' biography. It is she, more than anyone else, who turned Sharp's thought into a rather sterile orthodoxy.

In the short term, I think Sharp's influence on education was significant. As a schoolchild of the 1950s, my impression is that I first came across Sharp's name when singing from *English Folk-Songs for Schools*. Sharp did, for a time, have a direct influence on educational practice. Judging from the frustration evident in his accounts of inspecting folk dance and song among trainee teachers, I am not sure he would have judged his influence to have been a success. In the longer term, it has evaporated.

Perhaps because of its name, it is not always realised that the basis of the Vaughan Williams Memorial Library was Sharp's own library, which he left to the English Folk Dance Society on his death with the stipulation that it was to be made available to the public. Building on this excellent foundation, the library is now the foremost archive and place of reference for material on traditional dance and song, a unique and infinitely valuable resource. (It has been underfunded over many years and there is a danger of the permanent loss of unique material if significant investment is not forthcoming.)

And we have an institution, the English Folk Dance and Song Society, and a building-cum-monument, Cecil Sharp House. Like all institutions, it has gone through periods of expansion and contraction. The building, although of listed status, is in need of major refurbishment.

Acolytes and iconoclasts: interest in and interpretations of Sharp's work

Sharp was a great controversialist and a pugnacious arguer. It is not at all surprising that he has created controversy and no small amount of heated argument. Sharp did battle with some of the great and the good of his day. He fell out with his employer at the Hampstead Conservatoire. He fell out with Sir Hubert Parry over a musical engagement. He fell out with C. V. Stanford and the Board of Education over folk songs in schools and the question of what exactly a folk song was. The Board later – a dozen years later – employed him. He fell out with his original partner and close friend, Charles Marson, although the reasons for this remain obscure. He fell out with his one-time collaborator in the instigation of the folk dance revival, Mary Neal, and the people who sided with her.

Sharp was not an easy man to get on with. On the other hand, he inspired tremendous affection and loyalty among his friends and followers. These included, most significantly, Ralph Vaughan Williams (sometimes a moderating influence on Sharp's excesses), Maud Karpeles, Douglas Kennedy, and Helen Kennedy. He was a charismatic individual who divided people in his own day, and it is clear that his legacy continues to cause divisions. He seems to have courted controversy, ever ready to write to the *Morning Post*, the *Daily Chronicle*, or *The Times* to state his views and challenge his opponents. To those who disagreed with him, all he seemed to do was repeat dogmas as if they were truths. The modest Frank Kidson commented about Sharp's 1907 book: 'Conjectures are not conclusions, for such must stand the scrutiny of men who want proofs.'[51]

Here is Sharp writing to Arthur Somervell (himself a significant educational reformer) who had objected to the 'cheap cant' which assumes that 'no one belongs to the English folk unless he is at the ploughtail'.[52] He recommended that Somervell

Vacate his armchair for a week or two, forget his theories, arm himself with a stout shovel and pick – for diamonds lie deep – betake himself to the country-side, visit the village taverns, sit in the thatched cottages of outlying hamlets and listen to the peasants singing their own folk-songs.

If he did so,

On his return home he will burn his banners with their strange devices of 'Tom Bowling', 'Casablanca', 'Home, sweet home', and the like, and forthwith enrol himself among the select company of the 'cheap canters'. A new world, the existence of which he has hitherto denied, will be opened before his eyes, and I incidentally shall gain also, for it will relieve me of the well-nigh hopeless task of trying to make him understand that the folk-song proper is a very different thing from the hybrid variety, or the 'composed' song which he now champions with such pathetic ardour.[53]

Sharp's visionary quality comes through, but visionaries can be off-putting and sometimes frightening. In a manuscript note written after Sharp's death, Somervell recalled some of his encounters with him:

C♯ abused me violently for my 'National Folksongs' – 'You are inculcating the children of England with the sickly virus of Tom Bowling' … (He came to stay with us at Broadway and hectored us so much that we mentally resolved not to ask him again.)

Somervell and Sharp did make up again:

About 1920 we became friends again. When FD [folk dance] was introduced into schools he came to me walking on eggs, hoped he would not be hurting my feelings if he interfered so far with the school curriculum. He was the missionary. I was the orthodox church.

Latterly he came to care little about the classics, the 3 B's [Bach, Beethoven, and Brahms] and all that.[54]

Somervell spoke at the 1925 meeting that launched the Cecil Sharp Memorial Fund.[55]

On a few occasions Sharp won over, or at least silenced, those who initially opposed him. He took as good as he gave. Here is Ernest Newman writing a rejoinder to Sharp's reply to Newman's essay on 'The Folk-Song Fallacy':

It seems to be an incorrigible habit with Mr. Sharp to parcel out everything and everybody into categories. He is not happy till he has – or fancies he has – us all nicely bottled and labelled. I have already pointed out the fallacies into which he has fallen through the too facile use of such terms as 'the' Frenchman, 'the' German, and so on. Now he has invented a new abstraction – 'the' critic, who, of course, must have his fixed 'characteristics' like 'the' Frenchman. He exhorts me to 'silence my analytical mind, and try to feel the beauty of the folk-song'. The naïve theory apparently is that the 'analytical mind' and the capacity to feel the beauty of a folk-song cannot co-exist in the same person. It is the old idea that a soft heart necessarily implies a soft head – that deep feeling is incompatible with clear thinking. I beg to assure Mr. Sharp that it is not necessarily so.[56]

A writer in the *Musical Times* thought Newman's the most notable of all the challenges to Sharp's theories.[57]

Sharp, I am sure, perceived himself as an outsider from the musical establishment. He encountered considerable, and often condescending, opposition from those in positions of musical power. He was, after all, attempting something quite profound – to shift the very basis on which we thought about music. W. M. K. Warren gives us a sense of Sharp's feelings of embattlement:

There was a time when Mr Sharp was accused of faking very cleverly the ancient song and [the accusers] argued also that the charm all lay in the accompaniment which Sharp put to them. People would not believe that this wealth of song really existed all unknown to themselves, among the old and often despised dwellers in the courts of our towns and cottages of our countryside. Others would speak contemptuously of the modes and tunes in which these beautiful melodies were composed, as simply relicts of a barbarous age and well left in their obscurity. But Mr Sharp was daunted by no such treatment; he was convinced that he was on the track of something that was priceless but soon would be lost and he never would give in.[58]

We forget at our peril that Sharp was a radical figure and certainly not a member of any establishment as we would understand it today.

Sending a copy of his pamphlet on *Folk Singing in Schools* to W. G. McNaught, editor of the *Musical Times* and a senior school inspector, Sharp wrote: 'After reading it – if you have the hardihood to do this – you will I know yearn for my scalp, even at this season of goodwill! But I can't help it. I am beyond the pale and past reformation!'[59] McNaught assured Sharp that he would read the pamphlet with an open mind.[60] Sharp was never employed by any of the major centres of musical learning, and when he did speak to such bodies he found himself received coolly and did not find the experience very comfortable. He described the Musical Society at the Royal College of Music as 'stodgy', and came away with the feeling that 'their views are completely opposed to mine'.[61]

He remained an outsider and developed his own institutional base.

When Fox Strangways was collecting information for the Sharp biography in the early 1930s, he got a range of responses from the adulatory to the highly critical. Many people who had encountered Sharp thought very highly of him and stressed his kindness, generosity, warmth, and interest in them. Other, more critical testimonies offered rather different views of Sharp and point forward to more recent debates. His biographers, however, tended not to draw too much on those more negative accounts. Roland Heath, a friend and colleague, thought Sharp was a fanatic who could not keep off the subject of folk dancing:

As a fanatic, he inspired enthusiasm and affection wherever he went. He went too far, of course: fanatics do, and that was why he succeeded. And in the process he aroused opposition, some of it very bitter. But he was also a scholar: his knowledge of the grounds of his beliefs was profound, and his thought on them continuous and intense. For anyone who disliked folk dancing on purely aesthetic grounds to argue with him was extremely dangerous; he knew far too much about it. And even his most violent opponents, once they had met him and talked to him, were compelled to admit his knowledge, his mental capacity and his perfect sincerity.[62]

Not everyone agreed in their estimate of Sharp's knowledge. Sir Richard Terry (himself a one-time folk song collector) gave a frank account of his feelings and an analysis of what he thought was wrong with Sharp's work:

My chief objection to (the later) Sharp is his inaccuracy. He started all right in the folk-song business, but when he found himself in the position of High Priest of a cult he succumbed to the necessity of becoming an oracle. He invested (or rather, enveloped) the simplest things with that halo of mystery which so fascinates female devotees.

He was neither a folk-lorist nor an anthropologist, but he had to keep up the pose of being both. Once having formulated a theory it became a dogma with his following, and he was more or less forced into the position of having to make his folk-song 'facts' fit his folk-lore theories.[63]

We do not have to accept Terry's verdict at face value (which is not to deny that it may have some truth in it), but it is interesting that a prominent musician held such a view during Sharp's life and soon after his death.

By the 1930s and 1940s, when Vaughan Williams' star was in the ascendant and while he was representing Sharpian views in his American lectures,[64] many younger composers and critics became hostile to or dismissive of the idea of composition based on folk song. Constant Lambert decried the 'heartiness' of compositions in the national idiom, with their 'irritating sense of artificiality'.[65] Perhaps more interestingly, the young Benjamin Britten, who was to make a popular success of his settings of traditional songs for tenor and piano, distanced himself significantly from the nationalist movement.[66]

What Terry had described as a cult became a national institution, the English Folk Dance and Song Society, with its headquarters named after Cecil Sharp. It necessarily became an organisation that was concerned with its own work and survival, proselytising but also rather inward-looking. Significant members such as Maud Karpeles and Douglas Kennedy kept the banner of Sharpian orthodoxy alive and circulating, although EFDSS members undertook only a small amount of collecting. The American folk song scholar D. K. Wilgus commented in 1959: 'A part of the problem lay in the inflexible attitude of the Society. It is now apparent that England still contained folksong, but little that the Society considered worthy of preservation. Maud Karpeles and others continued to echo the conclusions and restrictions of Sharp.'[67]

By the time Wilgus was writing, the stirrings of the second folk song revival were under way. The magazine *Ethnic* had started making criticisms both of the EFDSS and of Sharp. A. L. Lloyd's *Folk Song in England* (1967) used Sharp's ideas, was fulsome in its praise of him, and also tried to transcend his thinking in the way we understand folk song.[68] Frank Howes' *Folk Music of Britain and Beyond* (1969) was not

really an answer to Lloyd, but was in many ways an informed statement of the Sharp tradition. Howes had been a long-standing member of the EFDSS and for a number of years the editor of its journal, as well as working as a music journalist. It was only in 1972, though, that a significant break with the past occurred with the publication of Dave Harker's 'Cecil Sharp in Somerset: Some Conclusions'.[69] The essay was, and was intended to be, iconoclastic. It was a critique of Sharp which concentrated on what Harker saw as a misrepresentation of the culture of working people in early twentieth century Somerset and on the way the collector had presented that culture to a wider public. Harker produced later work on this subject, most significantly his book *Fakesong* (1985), which contains many of the same arguments. I have been criticised for writing that Harker's work was the 'beginning of serious critical work' on the early folk music movement. I stand by that statement. I think Harker's work was serious and critical, but this does not mean that Harker got it all right.

In 1980, I produced an essay on the first English folk revival, 'Folk Song Collecting in Sussex and Surrey, 1843–1914'. At the time, I was undertaking a doctoral study of music and music-making in nineteenth-century Sussex. I wanted to assess how far the evidence produced by the folk song collectors was reliable as historical source material. I was also interested in the first folk song revival as a movement. Collectors, after all, shared ideas and motivations. I was concerned about the concentration on Sharp – a sort of cult of personality, if you like – which had dominated the subject. As it was, Sharp did little collecting in Sussex and so had only a minor role in my paper. In 1993, Georgina Boyes produced *The Imagined Village: Culture, Ideology and the English Folk Revival*. It is an interesting book, highly stimulating if uneven in its quality and disputable in some of its interpretations. It was a pioneering work in that it attempted to provide a history of twentieth-century folk revivals. (It was certainly not, as some have accused, merely a version of Harker.) Much of the book focuses on Sharp, his legacy, and the movement that he created around him. Sharp does not come out of it well: he is

Ralph Vaughan Williams

presented as the autocratic male leader of a predominantly female movement. This movement was peopled by 'classical musicians, schoolteachers and his personal following among the upper middle-class'. The basis of his career was making 'vernacular arts fit bourgeois aesthetics'.[70] In contrast, Gordon Cox's *A History of Music Education in England 1872–1928* (1993) sees Sharp in a generally more positive light, as an informed and progressive music educator who acted as a catalyst for the liberalisation of music education. To Cox, Sharp was a 'significant transitional figure' who helped music education advance from the rote methods of the nineteenth century towards a more imaginative approach.[71]

By the mid-1990s Sharp's reputation may have been at something of a low ebb after the depredations of Harker and Boyes, but a knight in shining armour was poised to rescue him in the shape of C. J. Bearman. Bearman's work is well informed, interesting, and adversarial. It is a strange mixture of sound common sense and fury. At its best it is very good indeed, but at times he seems to have been inspired by some of Cecil Sharp's less temperate outbursts. Of particular interest is his article in *Folklore*,

'Cecil Sharp in Somerset: Some Reflections on the Work of David Harker'. Here, Bearman claims to have shown that Harker's account of Sharp is 'inaccurate, innumerate, flawed in its methods, and unjustified in its assumptions'.[72] This is lively stuff and worthy of Sharp at his most outspoken. Bearman, as ever, makes some very good points. His 'Who Were the Folk? The Demography of Cecil Sharp's Somerset Folk Singers' deals in detail with the singers represented in this book.[73] He argues that it is wrong to see folk song as 'the cultural property of the working class' and shows that songs were current among a more diverse spectrum of society than the term 'working class' implies. (This is argued even though occupations such as agricultural labourer and general labourer loom large among Sharp's informants.) I have not space to analyse these articles' strengths and weaknesses but I urge readers to seek them out and read them, as well as Harker's originals. They will not be bored!

There has been some excellent work, particularly in the writings of Roy Judge, centring on Sharp's interest in folk dance. In contrast to some who have written about Sharp, Judge was a judicious and temperate writer as well as being an excellent scholar. His work on the rift between Sharp and Mary Neal is beautifully done, and his essay on the development of Sharp's interest in the morris shows the writer at the height of his abilities. Other scholars are worthy of mention. Theresa Buckland insightfully places Sharp in context in a review article on English folk dance scholarship.[74] John Francmanis' work is primarily on Frank Kidson of Leeds but nonetheless contains a lot about Sharp.[75] Paul Burgess has written on how Sharp discovered Gloucestershire morris.[76] Even I have been unable to resist the lure of this strange and fascinating man: I have lectured on him and hope to publish some pieces on his educational work in the future.

Within a few weeks of writing this essay I noticed that Mike Yates, a major English folk song collector of the post-war period, has written a recanting article influenced by C. J. Bearman's work on Harker and stating his admiration for Sharp's achievements.[77] And so it goes round, and round. Interest in and controversy over Sharp's work is alive and well and being carried on much in the same spirit in which Sharp conducted his own debates when he was alive. A man that can inspire controversy three-quarters of a century after his death has certainly had an influence and left an impression. The centre of a great deal of that controversy and interest is the work he did in Somerset and north Devon in the early years of the twentieth century. The songs he collected there and the lives of the singers who gave them to him are a source of interest and fascination in their own right, and they have been, and continue to be, the focus of much argument and discussion.

May 2003[78]

Footnotes

1   Mike Yates, 'Cecil Sharp in America: Collecting in the Appalachians', *Musical Traditions*, Article MT052 http://www.mustrad.org.uk/articles/sharp.htm (accessed 14 May 2003).

2   Hugh Anderson, 'Virtue in a Wilderness: Cecil Sharp's Australian Sojourn', *Folk Music Journal*, 6 (1994), 617–52.

3   Anderson, p. 618, referring to A. H. Fox Strangways in collaboration with Maud Karpeles, *Cecil Sharp* (London: Oxford University Press, 1933), and subsequent editions.

4   Anderson, p. 625.

5   Fox Strangways, p. 52.

6   Fox Strangways, pp. 26–28; Bob Grant, 'When Punch Met Merry', *Folk Music Journal*, 7 (1999), 644–55.

7   Fox Strangways, p. 33.

8   Box 4, Folder A, Item 1, Cecil Sharp Correspondence, VWML.

9   Cecil J. Sharp, ed., *A Book of British Song for Home and School* (London: John Murray, 1902), pp. vi.

10 W. M. K. Warren to Maud Karpeles, 15 November 1926, Box 4, Folder A, Item 20, Cecil Sharp Correspondence, VWML.

11 Annual Report of the Folk-Song Society, June 1904.

12 Bertrand Harris Bronson, *The Ballad as Song* (Berkeley and Los Angeles: University of California Press, 1969), p. 249.

13 Roy Judge, 'Mary Neal and the Esperance Morris', *Folk Music Journal*, 5 (1989), 545–91.

14 Roy Judge, 'Cecil Sharp and Morris 1906–1909', *Folk Music Journal*, 8 (2002), 195–228.

15 Vic Gammon, 'One Hundred Years of the Folk-Song Society', forthcoming in *Folk Song: Tradition, Revival, and Re-Creation*, ed. Ian Russell and David Atkinson [2003].

16 Warren to Karpeles, 15 November 1926.

17 David E. Whisnant, *All That Is Native & Fine: The Politics of Culture in an American Region*, The Fred W. Morrison Series in Southern Studies (Chapel Hill and London: University of North Carolina Press, 1983), p. 116.

18 Cecil J. Sharp, *Ballad Hunting in the Appalachians: Extracts of Letters Written by Cecil J. Sharp* (Boston: Todd [printer], 1916), p. 9 (27 August 1916) (Box 7, Folder B, Item 19, Cecil Sharp Correspondence, VWML), reproduced in Yates, 'Cecil Sharp in America'.

19 Cecil Sharp to Miss Scoville, 12 September 1917, Box 7, Folder B, Item 14, Cecil Sharp Correspondence, VWML.

20 See, for example, his pamphlet *Ballad Hunting in the Appalachians* (27 August 1916).

21 Michael Yates, 'Percy Grainger and the Impact of the Phonograph', *Folk Music Journal*, 4 (1982), 269; Erika Brady, *A Spiral Way: How the Phonograph Changed Ethnography* (Jackson: University of Mississippi, 1999).

22 E. C. Cawte, 'Watching Cecil Sharp at Work: A Study of His Records of Sword Dances Using His Field Notebooks', *Folk Music Journal*, 8 (2003), p. 282 and *passim*.

23 Vic Gammon, 'Folk Song Collecting in Sussex and Surrey, 1843–1914', *History Workshop Journal*, no. 10 (1980), 68.

24 *Daily Chronicle*, 24 May 1906.

25 *Morning Post*, 21 December 1906.

26 Cecil Sharp to Mr Pitchford, 13 April 1922, Box 2, Cecil Sharp Correspondence, VWML.

27 Peter Burke, *Popular Culture in Early Modern Europe*, revised reprint (Aldershot: Ashgate, 1994), p. 4.

28 Richard M. Dorson, *The British Folklorists: A History* (London: Routledge & Kegan Paul, 1968).

29 Cecil J. Sharp, *English Folk-Song: Some Conclusions* (London: Simpkin; Novello; Taunton: Barnicott & Pearce, 1907), p. 130.

30 Cecil J. Sharp, *Folk Singing in Schools* (London: English Folk Dance Society, n.d. [1913]), p. 7.

31 Sharp, *Folk Singing in Schools*, p. 14.

32 Sharp, *A Book of British Song for Home and School*, pp. vi.

33 Sharp, *English Folk-Song: Some Conclusions*, p. 133.

34 Sharp, *English Folk-Song: Some Conclusions*, p. 132.

35 Sharp, *Folk Singing in Schools*, p. 13.

36 A. L. Lloyd, *Folk Song in England* (London: Lawrence and Wishart, 1967), pp. 15–17.

37 Sharp, *English Folk-Song: Some Conclusions*, pp. 16–31.

38 Sharp, *English Folk-Song: Some Conclusions*, p. 16.

39 Sharp, *English Folk-Song: Some Conclusions*, p. 16.

40 Sharp, *English Folk-Song: Some Conclusions*, p. 21.

41 Sharp, *English Folk-Song: Some Conclusions*, p. 23.

42 Sharp, *English Folk-Song: Some Conclusions*, p. 29.

43 Ernest Newman, 'The Folk-Song Fallacy', *English Review*, 11 (May 1912), p. 259.

44 Quoted in Whisnant, p. 115.

45 Maud Karpeles to Mrs Storrow, 4 November 1917, Box 7, Folder B, Item 32, Cecil Sharp Correspondence, VWML.

46 *Musical Times*, 1 September 1910, p. 596; *Stratford-upon-Avon Herald*, 12 August 1910. I thank John Francmanis for this reference.

47 Quoted in Fox Strangways, p. 91.

48 Sharp, *English Folk-Song: Some Conclusions*, p. 135.

49 Sharp, *English Folk-Song: Some Conclusions*, pp. 138–39.

50 *Cecil Sharp's Collection of English Folk Songs*, ed. Maud Karpeles, 2 vols (London: Oxford University Press, 1974).

51 *Musical Herald*, August 1913, p. 228. I owe this splendid quote to the kindness of John Francmanis.

52 *Musical Times*, 1 December 1906, p. 807.

53 *Musical Times*, 1 December 1906, p. 808.

54 Box 4, Folder I, Item 29, Cecil Sharp Correspondence, VWML.

55 Typescript, 18 May 1925, Box 7, Folder F, Item 2, Cecil Sharp Correspondence, VWML.

56 Ernest Newman, 'The Folk-Song Fallacy: A Rejoinder', *English Review*, 12 (August 1912), p. 65.

57 *Musical Times*, 1 October 1912, p. 642.

58 Warren to Karpeles, 15 November 1926.

59 Cecil Sharp to W. G. McNaught, 29 December 1913, Box 2 (filed under Novello), Cecil Sharp Correspondence, VWML.

60 W. G. McNaught to Cecil Sharp, 29 December 1913, Box 2 (filed under Novello), Cecil Sharp Correspondence, VWML.

61 Cecil Sharp to Mrs Oppe, 1 August 1920, Box 2, Cecil Sharp Correspondence, VWML.

62 Roland Heath to A. H. Fox Strangways, 22 July 1931, Box 2, Cecil Sharp Correspondence, VWML.

63 Sir R. R. Terry to A. H. Fox Strangways, 2 November 1932, Box 3, Cecil Sharp Correspondence, VWML.

64 Ralph Vaughan Williams, *National Music*, The Mary Flexner Lectures on the Humanities, II (London: Oxford University Press, 1934).

65 Constant Lambert, *Music Ho!: A Study of Music in Decline* (London: Penguin, 1934), p. 123.

66 Benjamin Britten, 'England and the Folk-Art Problem', *Modern Music*, January–February 1941, pp. 71–75 (I owe this reference to John Francmanis).

67 D. K. Wilgus, *Anglo-American Folksong Scholarship Since 1898* (New Brunswick, Rutgers University Press, 1959), p. 132.

68 Vic Gammon, 'A. L. Lloyd and History: A Reconsideration of Aspects of *Folk Song in England* and Some of His Other Writings', in *Singer, Song and Scholar*, ed. Ian Russell (Sheffield: Sheffield University Press, 1986), pp. 147–64.

69 David Harker, 'Cecil Sharp in Somerset: Some Conclusions', *Folk Music Journal*, 2 (1972), 220–40.

70 Georgina Boyes, *The Imagined Village: Culture, Ideology and the English Folk Revival*, Music and Society (Manchester: Manchester University Press, 1993), p. 113 and *passim*.

71 Gordon Cox, *A History of Music Education in England 1872–1928* (Aldershot: Scolar Press, 1993), p. 160, and pp. 131–61 *passim*.

72 C. J. Bearman, 'Cecil Sharp in Somerset: Some Reflections on the Work of David Harker', *Folklore*, 113 (2002), 11–34.

73 C. J. Bearman, 'Who Were The Folk? The Demography of Cecil Sharp's Somerset Folk Singers', *Historical Journal*, 43 (2000) 751–75.

74 Theresa Buckland, 'Traditional Dance Scholarship in the United Kingdom', in *Dance – A Multicultural Perspective*, ed. Janet Adshead, Report of the Third Study of Dance Conference: University of Surrey, 5–9 April 1984 (Guildford: National Resource Centre for Dance, University of Surrey, for the Dance Research Unit, 1984), pp. 54–64.

75 E.g. John Francmanis, 'National Music to National Redeemer: The Consolidation of a "Folk Song" Construct in Edwardian England', *Popular Music*, 21 (2002), 1–25.

76 Paul Burgess, 'The Mystery of the Whistling Sewermen: How Cecil Sharp Discovered Gloucestershire Morris Dancing', *Folk Music Journal*, 8 (2002), 178–94.

77 Mike Yates, 'Jumping to Conclusions', *Musical Traditions*, Enthusiasms no. 36 http://www.mustrad.org.uk/enthuse.htm, (accessed 13 May 2003).

78 I would like to thank the following people: John Francmanis for conversations and for sharing so much of his work with me; Malcolm Taylor for his help and support with this essay; Luke Windsor for checking a section about transcription and ideas derived from the psychology of music; David Atkinson for his careful editing; and Sheila Gammon for proofreading, comments, and a great deal else.

THE REVEREND CHARLES LATIMER MARSON (1859-1914)

Marson was the eldest son of the Reverend Charles Marson, parish priest (1871-95) in Clevedon, Somerset. Charles junior went to Clifton College and studied classics and history at University College, Oxford, where he became a radical. Torn between journalism and the Church, Marson went to work at the Whitechapel Settlement in the East End of London with the Reverend Samuel Barnett. For two years he saw the miserable housing and terrible poverty of the parish, but also the innovative attempts by his colleagues to uplift the people – adult education classes, co-operative workshops, youth clubs and other social experiments. These ideas led Marson into the growing Christian Socialist movement. He became editor of *The Christian Socialist* magazine and was a founder of The Christian Socialist League.

In May 1889, a month after becoming engaged to Clotilda Bayne, a student at Newnham College, Cambridge, he left to take up a post in Australia and they were married a year later. Marson was one of the founders of the Labour Party in Adelaide and it was at this time that he met and became friends with Cecil Sharp. They had much in common but had not found a focus for their talents and energies. Both men were also struggling to overcome the handicap of chronic asthma.

In 1892 Marson returned to work in the London slums but his health broke down and so, in 1895, he was appointed by the Liberal Prime Minister to the crown living as curate of Hambridge. This was not a prestigious post and he did not like rural life initially, missing his London networks. On the other hand, he was in tune with 'back to the land' ideas and was prepared to learn country ways. He was a model parish priest, visiting his parishioners, teaching in the village school and running socials.

Marson had kept in touch with Cecil Sharp in London and in 1893 officiated at Sharp's wedding. Then, in August 1903, Marson invited Sharp to stay at Hambridge vicarage and, after the noting of *The Seeds of Love*, introduced Sharp to a number of other local singers. The two men loved the 'new music' and collaborated on the first three volumes of *Folk Songs from Somerset*, Marson editing the words and Sharp doing the musical arrangements. Indeed, it could be said that Marson's contribution to the first folk revival has perhaps been underestimated, even though he drifted away from Sharp after this intense early period of collecting.

Marson was one of a small number of High Church Socialists – his friends included Stewart Headlam and Conrad Noel, the 'Red Vicar' of Thaxted – with singular views on the changing role for the Church in an increasingly secular society. He was a charismatic figure, a realist with a sharp sense of humour and a stimulating perspective. He was in demand as a literary reviewer and was the author of numerous books and pamphlets, notably *Psalms at Work* (1894) (four editions), *Glastonbury or The English Jerusalem* (1909) and *God's Co-operative Society* (1914).

He died of heart failure following a sudden asthma attack in March 1914, aged 54.

David Sutcliffe

NOTES ON THE SELECTION OF SONGS AND MUSIC

The process of selecting songs for this book started with the music. The brief was to choose songs that were good to sing. Inevitably, the final selection is very personal.

Sharp's manuscripts contain a total of 4,977 folk tune (FT) notations, not all of course songs. However, narrowing 'only' the song- related tunes down to a meagre 50 has been a daunting task, but also a very enjoyable and stimulating one. As I worked through the manuscripts, I found myself sharing in Sharp's collecting journeys. Starting in Somerset, and making frequent return visits to the county, I then found myself somewhere else and telling friends, 'We're in Sussex today'.

It is well known that Somerset was a significant county for Sharp. He collected around 1,500 songs there and also noted significant numbers in other south western counties – Cornwall, Devon and Gloucestershire. But while his collecting visits in Somerset and to the Southern Appalachian mountain region of the USA have been well documented, it is not so well known that he in fact noted songs in many other areas of England. We have reflected this to a degree in this book.

It was obvious from the outset that other criteria needed to be set beyond the general 'singableness' of the songs. For example *The Seeds of Love*, the first song to be noted by Sharp, had to be included for its sheer significance (it is a happy chance that we have also included the last, Mrs Truby's version of *Three Maids A-Milking*). While other songs, many of which are a great pleasure to sing and which have become very well known (such as Mrs Sweet's *Searching for Lambs*, Harry Richards' *Just As the Tide Was A-Flowing* and Mrs Lock's *High Germany*), have been omitted purely because they have become so well known.

Other categories of song warrant their own publications. We have therefore excluded children's songs, sea shanties and all the songs collected by Sharp in the Southern Appalachians.

I urge the reader to look carefully at the tunes for these songs. You may think that you know them well – but look again! Some titles may be familiar – *The Foggy Dew, Farewell He, Banks of Claudy, John Barleycorn* – but the tunes may be less familiar. In other cases, you may just find a couple of notes that you weren't expecting, and if you are anything like me those notes will stimulate and excite you beyond measure. *Brimbledown Fair* is a case in point. Compare the tune to that of *Ramble Away*, and see how just a couple of notes in bar 3 and the last 5 notes of the verse add a subtle beauty and poignancy to the song.

Look at the songs, listen to the old singers, and then make the songs your own. Sing them as part of your daily life, as you mow your lawn or drive to work or rock your grandchildren, as well as when you perform. Let the tradition influence and mould your own stylistic approach to the songs.

These songs are not dusty old relics of times past. They are to be sung today. Enjoy singing them and remember that we all have a role in ensuring that they are passed on to new generations of singers. Tradition really is still growing.

Eddie Upton

NOTES ON THE SINGERS

Cecil Sharp's manuscripts were a prime source of biographical information about the singers, as were his published works and the general publicity and reportage of his work in a wide variety of contemporary periodicals. In addition to these materials, which are easily accessible at the Vaughan Williams Memorial Library, we utilised our own research into the localities of many of the singers and our personal gleanings from relatives and neighbours. As far as we know, none of the singers featured in *Still Growing* survived into the second half of the twentieth century, but we have been lucky enough to be in contact with a number of people who danced for, sang for, or provided accommodation for Mr Sharp.

As will become obvious throughout, another chief source of information was the 1901 census for England and Wales, now available on-line (http://www.census.pro.gov.uk). This, together with the 1891 version, helped us fill in some elusive gaps in our knowledge and extend our grasp of the towns and villages mentioned. Other important printed sources are cited throughout.

Being primarily interested in Somerset and Devon and their environs, we were very grateful for the contributions of Paul Burgess, Keith Chandler and Andy Turner, who covered the areas in which we were less knowledgeable. Their pieces bear their names.

Last but not least, we are indebted to Dave Bland for access to his research notes for a book on Sharp's singers which, regrettably, never materialised. These papers proved invaluable to us and are to be found at the Vaughan Williams Memorial Library where the librarians supervise access.

Bob & Jacqueline Patten

EDITING THE TEXTS

It is well known that Cecil Sharp, in line with most of his contemporaries, was more interested in the tunes of folk songs than the words, and he often noted down the music with only one verse of text – especially when he had previously collected a version of the song from another singer. In addition, many of his singers only supplied odd verses rather than full songs, and it is not always clear whether they had always sung the song that way, or had forgotten parts of it.

This leaves the potential editor in a perpetual quandary about how to treat the texts of the songs in a work aimed at the popular, as opposed to academic, reader. Sharp himself frequently combined the words from different versions to publish an ideal composite text, and even, on occasion, supplied new words to fill gaps, or deliberately omitted verses to 'soften' the rough edges of songs too outspoken for the readership of the time. Such editorial

practices are much less acceptable these days, and although we now have sufficient material to hand to make it relatively easy to cobble together versions, we have been reluctant to do so. We have found that it is rarely possible to combine texts without doing violence to each constituent version, so we have adopted a much lighter editorial hand, leaving it up to the reader to decide how much combination s/he wishes to do.

Where Sharp collected one verse only, we have simply given that verse, with the tune, and added a 'full' text from another of Sharp's singers, or another source. Where a singer's text was obviously 'fragmentary', we have again chosen to print those fragments, along with another text for comparison. Often the 'fragments' make perfectly acceptable songs in their own right. We have therefore made some minor corrections, and also left many 'rough edges' which other editors would have decided to change.

It should always be borne in mind that there is a world of difference between reading a traditional song text and hearing it sung. We have listed any changes or additions in the notes. In only one case have we made a deliberate change to suit modern sensibilities, in the song *Long Tailed Blue*.

We have not attempted to give the history of each song, and the notes are little more than a taster of what could be said. Nowadays we are blessed with a wealth of material on folk song, and to help anyone interested in following up other versions, or the history of the songs included in this book, we have supplied the standard numbers which will help them to get started: **Child** numbers refer to Francis James Child, *The English and Scottish Popular Ballads* (1882–1898); **Laws** numbers refer to G. Malcolm Laws, *American Balladry from British Broadsides* (1957); **Roud** numbers refer to Steve Roud, *Folk Song Index* (electronic database), available on subscription or for consultation at the Vaughan Williams Memorial Library and other folklore institutions in Britain and America.

Steve Roud

A NOTE ON SHARP MATERIALS

Throughout this book you will see many references to Cecil Sharp's collections. Whereas the photographs are easy to identify, finding a path through his manuscripts, papers and other miscellaneous materials can be a little difficult for the uninitiated. I hope the following descriptions will help.

Field Notebooks
Sharp's method of collecting songs was to have separate notebooks into which he would record tunes and words. It is from these field notebooks that he transcribed most of the material which is to be found in his fair copy manuscript collection (see below).

The field notebooks are a fascinating insight into the way that Sharp worked.

Manuscripts
Divided again into tunes and words, these fair copy transcriptions from the field notebooks were bequeathed to Clare College, Cambridge, and still reside there. Microfilm and bound hard copies exist at the Vaughan Williams Memorial Library (VWML), where they are referred to most often. These are the manuscripts herein called Folk Tunes (FT) and Folk Words (FW), and their reference numbers appear after the biography of each singer included.

Correspondence
In the preparation of Cecil Sharp's biographies, many of his letters were recovered from recipients and added to the surviving letters received by Sharp. These, together with rough copies of letters sent by Sharp and those to his biographers after his death, were sorted into two sequences – one alphabetical and one classified by subject. Added to these were some miscellaneous cuttings, leaflets and pamphlets, as well as some rough drafts of articles. Of particular interest here is a folder entitled Collecting Folksong.

Miscellaneous
The heterogeneous nature of these seven boxes of materials has resulted in this vague title. Here are collected together his original compositions and arrangements, Appalachian materials (including his diaries and the manuscripts of Olive Dame Campbell), lectures, notebooks and drafts, biographical materials, training college diaries and sword dance investigation correspondence.

Photographs
On a number of his collecting trips in England and North America, Sharp took with him a camera and left us with a small but outstanding collection of images of some of the many musicians and dancers he met. All of the photographs of singers in this book come from this collection, which was carefully arranged according to Sharp's original negative wallets by former librarian, Dave Bland. This collection forms part of a much more extensive collection held by the English Folk Dance and Song Society (EFDSS), which includes the many other portraits of Sharp and Marson reproduced here.

References to images in this collection appear after each biography.

Press Cuttings
Judging from the numerous volumes of press cuttings left to us by the Folk-Song Society and English Folk Dance Society, and indeed by Sharp himself, it seems clear that all parties were keenly aware of their impact throughout what is now known as the first folk music revival. Taken from the largest national organs to the most obscure of local periodicals, these cuttings books are a treasure trove of contemporary accounts and impressions of Sharp's work in progress.

With the exception of the *Manuscripts*, the originals of all of the above collections are housed at the Vaughan Williams Memorial Library. If consulting the manuscripts at Clare College, Cambridge, beware of some differences in referencing to those used by the VWML. For guidance on this issue see *Folk Music Journal, 8 (2002), 132–35.*

Malcolm Taylor

The Singers
&
the Songs

JACK BARNARD
Bridgwater, Somerset

Little is known about **Jack Barnard,** who lived in Bridgwater when he sang for Sharp, for the collector wrote few notes about him and he appears to have been missed by the 1901 census enumerator. However, the following extract from a letter written in 1931 to Sharp's biographer, A. H. Fox Strangways, by the Rev. Warren of Bridgwater, provides us with a graphic and moving picture of Jack:

There was a man (about 50), a cripple who had never been to school, called J Barnard, who sang over 150 songs. He could neither read or write, yet had a very accurate memory which Sharp tested in this way. There was a woman he had failed over and over again to get to sing. He put Barnard on to get her to sing to him, which he succeeded in doing, & then sang some of her songs to Sharp. At last Sharp got her to sing these songs to him & found that they [were] word for word & note for note the same as Barnard chanting [?] them to him.

The lady in question was Susan Clark, aged 82, who lived opposite Jack Barnard.

The next day Sharp noted two songs from Susan, but not the ones that Jack sang for him. Sharp may have chosen to concentrate on collecting songs to add to her repertoire rather than duplicate ones that he had heard from someone else.

THE BONNY LIGHT HORSEMAN

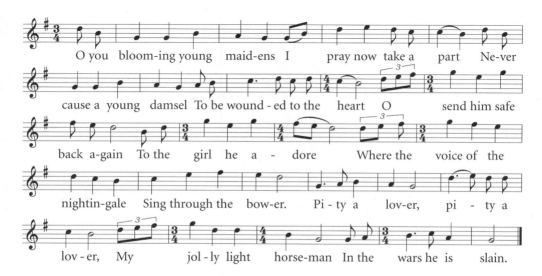

O you bloom-ing young maid-ens I pray now take a part Ne-ver cause a young damsel To be wound-ed to the heart O send him safe back a-gain To the girl he a - dore Where the voice of the nightin-gale Sing through the bow-er. Pi-ty a lov-er, pi-ty a lov-er, My jol-ly light horse-man In the wars he is slain.

THE BONNY LIGHT HORSEMAN

O you blooming young maidens
I pray now take a part
Never cause a young damsel
To be wounded to the heart
O send him safe back again
To the girl he adore
Where the voice of the nightingale
Sing through the bower.
Pity a lover, pity a lover,
My jolly light horseman
In the wars he is slain.

O eighteen months long by her I've been courted
Where sweethearts do walk and young lambs are sporting
Where me and my true love passed many long hours
Where the voice of the nightingale sang through the bower.

Broadside text

THE LIGHT HORSEMAN SLAIN IN THE WARS

Ye maidens, wives and widows, too, give attention,
Unto these few lines, tho' dismal to mention;
I'm a maiden distracted, in the deserts I'll rove,
To the gods I'll complain for the loss of my love.

Broken-hearted I wander, broken-hearted I wander
My bonny light-horseman is slain in the war.

Had I wings like an angel, so quickly I'd fly,
To the very spot where my true love did die,
On his grave would I flutter my out-stretch'd wings
And kiss his cold lips o'er and o'er again.

Two years and two months since he left England's shore,
My bonny light horseman that I did adore,
O why was I born, the sad day for to see,
When the drum beat to arms and did force him from me.

Not a Lord, Duke, or Earl, could my love exceed,
Nor a more finer youth for his king e'er did bleed,
When mounted on horse he so gay did appear,
And by all his regiment respected he were.

Like the dove that doth mourn when it loses its mate,
So will I for my love till I die for his sake,
Not a man on this earth my affections shall gain,
I'll a maid live and die for my love that was slain.

THE PRESS GANG

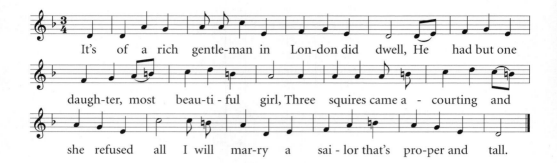

It's of a rich gentle-man in Lon-don did dwell, He had but one daugh-ter, most beau-ti-ful girl, Three squires came a - courting and she refused all I will mar-ry a sai - lor that's pro-per and tall.

It's of a rich gentleman in London did dwell,
He had but one daughter, most beautiful girl,
Three squires came a-courting and she
   refused all
'I will marry a sailor that's proper and tall.

Now father, dear father, now hinder me not,
I'll marry a sailor, I hope it will be my lot
To see him in his charm with a smile on his
   face
I'm sure that a sailor he is no disgrace.'

They walked out and they talked both night
   and day,
They walked and they talked and fixed the
   wedding day,
The old man overheard it and these words he
   did say:
'He shan't marry my daughter I'll press him
   to sea.'

As they was a-walking towards the church door
The press gang overtook him and from her
   him tore.
They pressed this young fellow all on the salt
   sea;
Instead of getting married he sorrowed for she.

She cut off her hair and she altered her clothes
And to the press master she immediately goes,
Saying: 'Press master, press master, do you
   want a man?
I am willing and ready to do all I can.'

Then she shipped on board of the very same
   ship
Her true love for a messmate so quickly she
   did take.
True love for a messmate, you quickly shall
   hear,
She sleep by his side for full half a year.

Now one morning, one morning as these two
   arose
They got into discourse as they put on their
   clothes.
'Once I had a sweetheart in London lived she,
But it's her cruel father that pressed me to sea.'

She looked in his face and looked him quite
   start
Say now, 'I believe you are my sweetheart,
For now we'll get married before our ship's
   crew
We won't care for father or all he can do.'

Twenty-nine songs were noted from Jack Barnard's repertoire of 150 and Sharp visited him on thirteen occasions between August 1906 and August 1909. Two songs were also noted from Jack's wife, Elizabeth.

-

Manuscript refs:
FT 961, 962, 1202, 1203, 1308-1310, 1350, 1351, 1354, 1357, 1384, 1551-1553, 1562, 1598, 1599, 1751-1753, 2014-2016, 2242, 2245-2248
FW 1004, 1008-1010, 1184, 1226-1228, 1251, 1252, 1277, 1278, 1397-1399, 1408, 1449, 1450, 1576-1581, 1879-1882, 2063-2071
Photo refs: B63

WILLIAM BAYLIS
Buckland, Gloucestershire

William 'Bill' Baylis was the illegitimate son of a farm labourer's daughter. Born in Stanton around 1847, he lived for most of his life in the village of Laverton, which is part of the parish of Buckland, near the Gloucestershire/Worcestershire border, where he too worked the land.

Sharp noted down a half dozen of Bill's songs on a single visit in April 1909. Indeed, Sharp recorded several singers in the area around Buckland, garnering a wide variety of material from children's games to ballads and carols. Percy Grainger also recorded some wax cylinders there, although he appears not to have met Baylis.

Bill married Matilda Andrews in 1867 and the couple had several children, none of whom stayed in the area. He died in 1926.

Paul Burgess

Manuscript refs:
FT 2131-2136
FW 2010-2012
Photo refs: A55

ON CHRISTMAS TIME

On Christ-mas time all Christ-ians sing To hear what news those Christ-ians bring; News of great joy, news of great mirth, News of our Sa-viour's own King's birth.

On Christmas time all Christians sing
To hear what news those Christians bring;
News of great joy, news of great mirth,
News of our Saviour's own King's birth.
 News of great joy, news of great mirth,
 News of our Saviour's own King's birth.

Then why should men on earth be so sad
Since our Redeemer made us glad
When from all sin he set us free
All for to gain our liberty.

Now sin depart this oldest life
Everlasting life comes in its place
And soon we shall our terror see,
And poor and rich must conquered be.

Then out of darkness we see light
Which makes all angels to sing this night:
Glory to God and peace to men
Both now and for evermore Amen.

JAMES BEALE
Warehorne, Kent

James Beale (1836-1918) was born at Wivelsfield in Sussex. According to Beale family tradition, he was a 'caravan-dweller' until settling at Hamstreet, Kent, on the edge of Romney Marsh – most likely by 1870. In the 1901 census he is shown as living at an unnumbered dwelling on the Ruckinge Road, Hamstreet, and is listed as a 'Wood and Timber Dealer', working on his own account (Kelly's Directory for 1903 records him as a poulterer, but no doubt he turned his hand to a variety of work). Living with him were his wife Charlotte and four grown-up sons – including Albert Beale, then 25, whom Peter Kennedy would record in the 1950s. From earlier census records it appears that James had eleven children in all; Albert recalled that his mother used to lead the choir in Hamstreet Chapel, and that there had at one time been no less than ten family members in the choir there.

Cecil Sharp visited Hamstreet and neighbouring villages on 23 September 1908. He took down songs from Charles Barling of Ruckinge, Clarke Lonkhurst and George Benstead of Hamstreet, as well as James Beale at Spothouse Farm, Warehorne. Mr Beale sang eight songs: *No John, No, The Woodman's Daughter, Stroll Away the Morning Dew (The Baffled Knight), Cold Blow and a Rainy Night, The Keys of Heaven, The Bold Fisherman, The Moon Shines Bright* and *Sons of Levi*. Sharp included the latter – a rarely-collected and rather strange song with possible Masonic overtones – in his *English Folk-Carols* and stated that: 'This carol is, and has been for many years, annually sung at Christmas in Ham Street and the neighbouring villages by a party of male carol singers.' Presumably, *The Moon Shines Bright* also formed part of these singers' repertoire, and we can add to this *As I Sat On A Sunny Bank* and *The Seven Joys of Mary*, since all three of these carols were collected by Sharp in 1911 from Mr Beale's married daughter, Alice Harden.

Peter Kennedy and Maud Karpeles visited Albert Beale on behalf of the BBC in January 1954, recording seven songs in all. Included amongst these was *The Moon Shines Bright* and Albert Beale can be heard singing this on *The Bitter Withy* (Folktracks cassette, 60-504). Bertie's younger brother James was also a good singer – 'He could sing best when he was half drunk … Oh he could sing' – but unfortunately does not appear to have had any of his songs collected.

Andy Turner

Manuscript refs:
FT 1922-1929
FW 1775-1787
Photo refs: none

*The Moon Shines Bright –
from Sharp's field notebook*

THE MOON SHINES BRIGHT

The moon shines bright, the stars give light A lit-tle be-fore it was day, The Lord our God he calls on us And bids us to wake and pray.

The moon shines bright, the stars give light
A little before it was day,
The Lord our God he calls on us
And bids us to wake and pray.

Awake, awake, good people all,
Awake and you shall hear
How our Lord our God died on the Cross
For us he loved so dear.

In yonder garden green doth grow
As green as any leek,
Our Lord our God he waters us
With his heavenly dew so sweet.

So teach your children well, dear man,
It's whilst that you are here.
It will be the better for your soul, dear man,
When you are gone from here.

Today you might be alive, dear man,
And worth ten thousand pound:
Tomorrow you might be dead, dear man,
And your corpse lie underground.

The turf all at your head, dear man,
And another at your feet,
When your good deeds and your bad deeds
Before the Lord will meet.

WILLIAM BRIFFETT
Bridgwater, Somerset

In the course of three visits during 1905 and 1907, **William Briffett** sang a total of thirteen songs for Sharp, none of which were published in *Folk Songs from Somerset*. Although Sharp recorded his age as 73 in 1907, the only available William Briffett in the 1901 census return would have been 50 in 1907, although this could be an enumerator's mistake. This William Briffett was a brickyard labourer living with his wife Elizabeth (48) and sons Willie (12) and Reginald (10) and five months old nephew, Tom Woodyatt. Judging from the photograph, this is not the same man.

Manuscript refs:
FT 550, 558, 1210-1220
FW 619, 620, 635, 636, 1186-1194
Photo refs: A15

THE PRIDE OF KILDARE

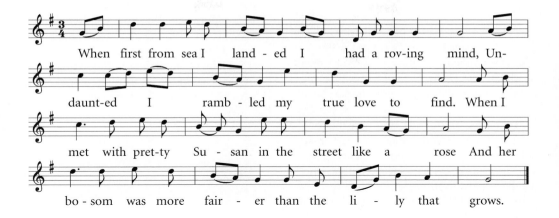

When first from sea I land-ed I had a rov-ing mind, Un-
daunt-ed I ramb-led my true love to find. When I
met with pret-ty Su - san in the street like a rose And her
bo - som was more fair - er than the li - ly that grows.

When first from sea I landed I had a roving mind,
Undaunted I rambled my true love to find.
When I met with pretty Susan in the street like a rose
And her bosom was more fairer than the lily that grows.

Her keen eyes did glitter like the bright stars by night,
And the robe she was wearing was costly and bright
And her bare neck was shaded with her long ravening hair,
And they calls her pretty Susan, the Pride of Kildare.

Long time I courted her till I wasted all my store,
Her love turned to hate me because I were poor.
She said: 'I will have another one whose fortune I'll share.
So begone from pretty Susan, the Pride of Kildare.'

'Twas early one morning as I lonely did stray
There I spied Susan with her young lad so gay,
And I passed by them with my mind full of care
Sighs for pretty Susan, the Pride of Kildare.

Once more on the ocean I'm resolved to go
And bound to West Indies with my heart full of woe,
There I beheld the ladies with jewels so rare,
There was none like pretty Susan, the Pride of Kildare.

Sometimes I am jovial, sometimes I am sad,
Since my love she's been courted by some other young lad.
But now I'm at a distance no more I'll despair,
But my blessings on my Susan, the Pride of Kildare.

WILLIAM BRISTER
Ilminster, Somerset

Cecil Sharp met **William Brister** at Ilminster Fair on 29 August 1905, when he noted three songs, only one of which, *The Twelve Days of Christmas*, was published in *Folk Songs from Somerset (Series Two)*.

At the time of the 1901 census, William lived in Ilminster and worked as a cattleman. He was 55 and had been born in Barrington, a village nearby. William's wife, Sophia, who had been born in Ilminster, was two years younger than him and they had five children and one granddaughter, Florence Brister, aged 2, living with them. The oldest daughter, Susan (24), had been born at Barrington while the other children, Emma (20), Henry (19), Ellen (15) and Jane (11), were all born in Ilminster.

William's connections with Barrington might account for his introduction to Sharp, who had already visited the village.

Manuscript refs:
FT 607-609
FW none
Photo refs: none

Brister's tunes for Twelve Days of Christmas and I'm Seventeen Come Sunday, noted by Sharp when 'W. B. was in his cups'

THE IRISH GIRL

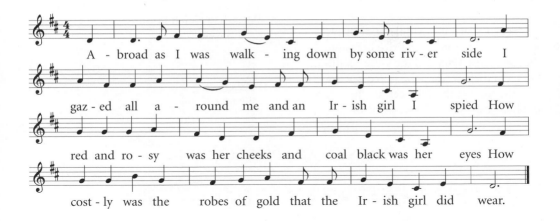

A - broad as I was walk - ing down by some riv - er side I
gaz - ed all a - round me and an Ir - ish girl I spied How
red and ro - sy was her cheeks and coal black was her eyes How
cost - ly was the robes of gold that the Ir - ish girl did wear.

Abroad as I was walking down by some river side
I gazed all around me and an Irish girl I spied
How red and rosy was her cheeks and coal black was her eyes
How costly was the robes of gold that the Irish girl did wear.

Full text from Henry Corbet of Snowshill, Gloucestershire

As I walked out one morning gay, down by a riverside,
I gazed all around me, an Irish girl I spied,
So red and rosy was her cheeks, and coal-black was her hair,
And so costly was the robes of white, my Irish girl did wear.

Her shoes were of the Spanish black, and spangled round with dew,
She wrung her hands and tore her hair, crying 'Alas what shall I do?
I'm going home, I'm going home, I'm going home' said she,
'Why will you go a-roving, and slight your own Polly?'

I wish I was a butterfly, I'd fly to my love's breast,
I wish I was a linnet, I'd sing to the lord and rest,
I wish I was a nightingale, I'd sing to the morning clear,
I'd sit and sing to my Polly, the girl I love so dear.

I wish I was at Exeter, all seated on the grass,
With a quart of wine all in my hand, and on my knee a lass,
I'd call for liquors merrily, and pay before I go,
And roll her in my arms once more, let the wind blow high or low.

ELLEN CARTER
Cheddar Cliffs, Somerset

Cecil Sharp visited **Ellen Carter** of Cheddar on at least two occasions, in August 1906 and the same month in 1908. On each occasion he noted one song.

At the time of the 1901 census she was 65, and her husband, Thomas, a general labourer, was 68. Their unmarried daughter, Eliza, aged 21, was still living with them, but their four sons, Charles, Jesse, Edward and Bevis, had all left home.

Manuscript refs:
FT 1085, 1787
FW none
Photo refs: none

'TWAS ON AN APRIL MORNING

'Twas on an Ap-ril morn-ing, just as the sun was ri - sing There did I hear some pret-ty birds did sing A - singing love-ly Nan - cy, all love it is a fan - cy Sweet was those notes that those pretty birds did sing.

'Twas on an April morning, just as the sun was rising
There did I hear some pretty birds did sing
A-singing lovely Nancy, all love it is a fancy
Sweet was those notes that those pretty birds did sing.

Second version from R. Bryant of Devon

'Twas on one April morning, just as the sun was rising
'Twas on one April morning, I heard the small birds sing.
They were singing, lovely Nancy, for love it is a fancy,
So sweet were the notes that I heard the small birds sing.

Young men are false, and full of deceiving;
Young men are false, and seldom do prove true;
For they're roving and they're ranging, and their minds are always changing,
For they're thinking for to find out, some pretty girl that's new.

O if I had but my own heart in keeping!
O if I had but my own heart back again!
Close in my bosom, I would lock it up for ever,
And it should wander never, so far from me again.

Why would you spend all your long time in courting?
Why would you spend all your long time in vain?
For I don't intend to marry, I'd rather longer tarry,
So young man, don't you spend all your long time in vain.

EMILY COCKRAM
Meshaw, Devon

Emily Cockram received one visit from Cecil Sharp on 9 January 1904, when he collected two songs: *The Gallant Huzzar* and *Lord Thomas and Fair Eleanor*.

The 1901 census return for Devon includes three Emily Cockrams, but none who are of the immediate area or likely age.

Manuscript refs:
FT 91-92
FW 153-158
Photo refs: none

THE GALLANT HUZZAR

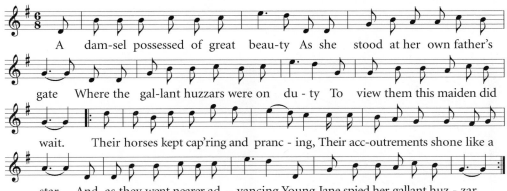

A damsel possessed of great beauty
As she stood at her own father's gate
Where the gallant huzzars were on duty
To view them this maiden did wait.
Their horses kept capering and prancing,
Their accoutrements shone like a star
As they went nearer advancing
Young Jane spied her gallant huzzar.

With their pelisses hung over their shoulders
How careless they seem for to ride.
O warlike appeared this young soldier
With their glittering swords by their side.
To the barracks next morning so early
This damsel she went in a car
Because that she loved him so dearly
Young Edward, her gallant huzzar.

And as she conversed with the soldiers
These words she was heard for to say:
'I've a heart no one bolder
To follow my laddie away.'
'Come, come', says Edward, 'be steady
And think of the dangers of war.
When the trumpet sounds I must be ready
So wed not your gallant huzzar.

Your parents you're bound for to mind them
Or else you're for ever undone.
They will leave you no portion behind them
So I pray you my company shun.'
Says she: 'If you will be true-hearted
I have gold at my uncle's in store.
From this time no more we'll be parted
And I'll wed with my gallant huzzar.'

As he gazed on her beautiful features
The tears they did fall from each eye.
'I will wed with this beautiful creature
And shun cruel wars,' he did cry.
And now they're united together
And think of them where they're afar.
God bless them now and for ever,
Young Jane and her gallant huzzar.

WILLIAM CORNELIUS
South Petherton, Somerset

William Cornelius does not feature in South Petherton in the 1901 census return and enquiries made around the village during the 1980s failed to identify him. Cornelius is a fairly common surname in the South Petherton/Shepton Beauchamp area. There were two men by the name of William Cornelius living in Somerset in 1901, both born and working in Chard. Neither is likely to be the singer. Our man may have been working away from the area at the time of the census and returned in retirement. Sharp visited William just the once, on 10 April 1907, and noted three songs.

Manuscript refs:
FT 1345-1347
FW 1244-1246
Photo refs: none

God Speed the Plough – from Sharp's field notebook

GOD SPEED THE PLOUGH

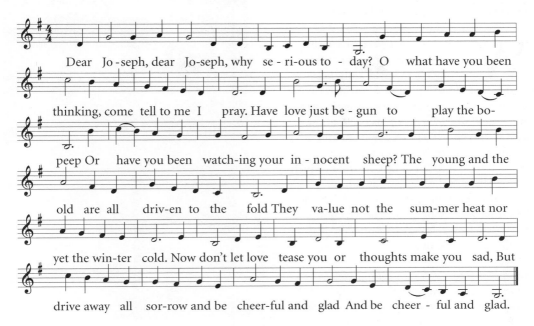

Dear Jo-seph, dear Jo-seph, why se-ri-ous to-day? O what have you been thinking, come tell to me I pray. Have love just be-gun to play the bo-peep Or have you been watch-ing your in-nocent sheep? The young and the old are all driv-en to the fold They va-lue not the sum-mer heat nor yet the win-ter cold. Now don't let love tease you or thoughts make you sad, But drive away all sor-row and be cheer-ful and glad And be cheer-ful and glad.

Dear Joseph, dear Joseph, why serious today?
O what have you been thinking, come tell to me I pray.
Have love just begun to play the bo-peep
Or have you been watching your innocent sheep?
The young and the old are all driven to the fold
They value not the summer heat nor yet the winter cold.
Now don't let love tease you or thoughts make you sad,
But drive away all sorrow and be cheerful and glad
And be cheerful and glad.

In old ancient days there was no cursed money,
The children of Israel eat milk and good honey,
No queen could be seen from the highest degree
They milk their brown cows and their sheep they often see.
Them lambs give them clothing the cows they give them milk
And that's how the farmer played all those good deeds.
Them lambs give them clothing the cows they give them milk
And that's how the farmer played all those good deeds
Played well all those good deeds

But as for old Adam how he work with the spade
And how he planted vineyards and neatly he made.
But as for the farmer with his love exposed
With beef and good bacon they could keep a good house
With a firkin in each corner from his own barley mow
He'd welcome in a friend and may God speed the plough.
With a firkin in each corner from his own barley mow
He'd welcome in a friend and may God speed the plough
And may God speed the plough.

William Cornelius 41

FREDERICK CROSSMAN
Huish Episcopi, Somerset

When he first met Cecil Sharp in 1904, **Frederick Crossman** was earning his living as a market gardener at Huish Episcopi, Somerset, having learnt his trade as a gardener in service at a 'big house'. On account of his occupation, he was known to some by the nickname 'Cauliflower' Crossman; others, however, referred to him as 'Singing' Crossman, which is why Sharp and Marson visited him. His musical activities stretched well beyond folk song, as he sang in the church choir and was a bell-ringer. Isabel Wyatt in *The Book of Huish* (*c.*1933) recorded:

When 'Singing' Crossman got married in 1867 he went straight from the vestry up to the bell-room to help ring his own wedding-peal; there were four generations of his family in the tower, he being the youngest. In 1927, being then 83 years old, he helped again to ring the bells on his sixtieth anniversary; again there were four generation of his family there, he this time the eldest.

Elsewhere in the same book she gives Frederick's opinion of Sharp: 'a proper pleasant-spoken gentleman, with a pipe in his mouth and a hole in his dancing shoon'.

She goes on to explain how some of the songs were noted with Frederick sitting on the trunk of a fallen apple tree in his orchard, with Sharp on one side noting the tunes and Marson on the other noting the words.

Finally, she tells us:

This singer has an inexhaustible repertoire of folk-songs, gathered in childhood from the withy-strippers in Wagg Drove. As a boy he saved his money for Bridgwater Fair, to spend, not 'on fairlings and such trade', but on the ballad-sheets sold by the ballad-singers whom the noise of the new roundabouts had driven away; these ballads it was his delight to 'study up' as he went about his work.

Frederick learnt his most well-known song, *As I Walked Through The Meadows*, from a 'ballet' bought at Bridgwater's Matthew's Fair. Other songs were learnt as a young man when he followed the harvest and went reaping on Salisbury Plain in Wiltshire.

Frederick's granddaughter, Amy Ford, helped her grandparents around the house as her grandmother, Maria, became increasingly frail. On Saturday mornings she used to accompany her grandfather on his 'veg round' in the Langport area. During these times she learnt many of her grandfather's songs and was recorded in later life by Bob and Jacqueline Patten. It is interesting to note that of the eleven songs that Sharp collected from Frederick's 'inexhaustible repertoire' between 1904 and 1909, only one was known to Amy Ford: *As I Walked Through The Meadows*, which appears in *Folk Songs from Somerset*.

Frederick Crossman died on 3 February 1933.

Manuscript refs:
FT 170-172, 228-231, 816-818, 2032
FW 257-262, 321-326, 614, 873, 874, 1901
Photo refs: B27

NEW YEAR'S SONG

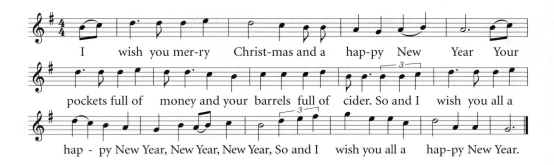

I wish you mer-ry Christ-mas and a hap-py New Year Your
pockets full of money and your barrels full of cider. So and I wish you all a
hap - py New Year, New Year, New Year, So and I wish you all a hap-py New Year.

I wish you merry Christmas and a happy New Year
Your pockets full of money and your barrels full of cider.
So and I wish you all a happy New Year, New Year, New Year,
So and I wish you all a happy New Year.

The old year is past and the New Year is come
And all the jolly soldiers are beating on the drum.

Here's a health to you in water, I wish it was in wine
And all the money you have got I'm sure it's none of mine.

Here's a health to our master and missus likewise
And all the pretty family around the fireside.

WE SERVING MEN GET PLEASURE

We serv-ing men get plea-sure And pas-time out of mea-sure For to
see the hare trip o - ver the plain. With our hors-es and our hounds make the
hills and val-leys sound That's the plea-sure for we serv - ing men.

We serving men get pleasure
And pastime out of measure
For to see the hare trip over the plain.
With our horses and our hounds
Make the hills and valleys sound
That's the pleasure for we serving men.

My pleasure's more than that
For to see my ox so fat
And some good stacks of hay round them
  stand.
With our horses and our hounds
We make the hills and valleys sound
That's the pleasure for we farmer men.

ONCE I COURTED A FAIR YOUNG WOMAN

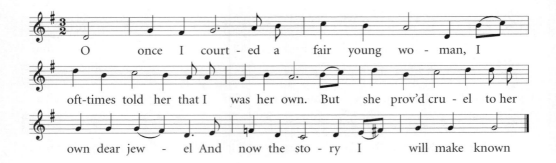

O once I courted a fair young woman,
I oft-times told her that I was her own.
But she proved cruel to her own dear jewel
And now the story I will make known

I went unto her cruel mother
Thinking in her I should find a friend.
She says: 'Begone, begone, O you roving,
For she has some other, you may depend.'

'Here's seven long years you've a-robbed my daughter,
Here's seven long years confined shall be,
Here's seven long years on bread and cold water
This cruel woman confined me.'

Now this fair damsel she has got married
To some roving blade of this town,
With his rattling, roaring and his best and boring**
Then he soon brought her proud stomach down.

So as I was going up to London city,
As I was going up through London straight one day,
So I saw her down at some door a-begging
As I myself was in a starving way.

So I put my hand into my pocket
So I gave to her all one half-crown.
So she cried and said, 'It is more unto me
Than unto thee it was five hundred pound.'

All you young maidens that goes a-courting,
Give a heed unto what I say,
So there's many a dark and cloudy morning
Turns out to be a sunshiny day.

**The singer said this was wrong, but he couldn't remember the correct words.

WILLIAM DURKIN
Ilminster, Somerset

Little is known of **William Durkin**. Sharp met him once, at Ilminster Fair, on 30 August 1905, the day of an eclipse of the sun, when he noted five songs. In a lecture on 14 December 1905, Sharp said: 'During the eclipse I took down songs from a ballad hawker in the wash house of a small Public House.' Of the three singers that he encountered on that day, two of them, William Brister and Thomas Hendry, were residents of Ilminster. Therefore, William Durkin was most probably the ballad hawker.

According to the 1901 census return, there were two William Durkins in the county of Somerset on the night of the census. One would have been aged 15 years old in 1905 and the other 21. It is unlikely that the singer, William Durkin, was one of these. As a ballad hawker, he may have come to the fair from far beyond the county.

Manuscript refs:
FT 610-614
FW none
Photo refs: none

Dream of Napoleon – from Sharp's field notebook

DREAM OF NAPOLEON

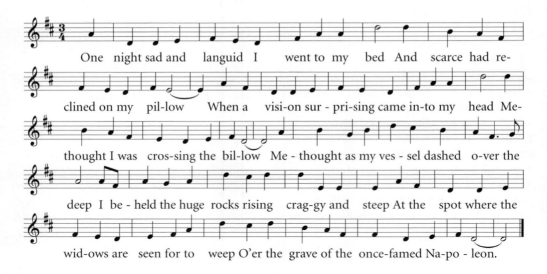

One night sad and languid I went to my bed And scarce had reclined on my pil-low When a visi-on sur-pri-sing came in-to my head Methought I was cros-sing the bil-low Me - thought as my ves - sel dashed o-ver the
deep I be - held the huge rocks rising crag-gy and steep At the spot where the
wid-ows are seen for to weep O'er the grave of the once-famed Na-po - leon.

One night sad and languid I went to my bed
And scarce had reclined on my pillow
When a vision surprising came into my head
Methought I was crossing the billow
Methought as my vessel dashed over the deep
I beheld the huge rocks rising craggy and
    steep
At the spot where the widows are seen for to
    weep
O'er the grave of the once-famed Napoleon.

I dreamt as my vessel she near'd to the land
I beheld clad in green his bold figure
The trumpet of fame he clasped firm in his
    hand
On his brow there sat valour and rigour
Oh stranger he cried hast thou ventur'd to
    me
From the land of the forefathers who boast
    they are free
If so a true story I'll tell unto thee
Concerning the once-famed Napoleon.

'Remember that year so immortal,' he cried
'When I crossed the rude Alps famed in story
With the legions of France, for her sons were
    my pride
And I led them to honour and glory
On the plains of Marengo I tyranny hurled
And whenever my banner the eagle unfurled
'Twas the standard of freedom all over the
    world
The signal of fame' – cried Napoleon.

'As a soldier I've borne both the heat and the
    cold
I have marched to the trumpet and cymbal
But by dark deeds of treachery I have been
    sold
Tho' monarchs before me did tremble
Now rulers and princes their stations demean
And like scorpions they spit forth their
    venom and spleen
But liberty soon o'er the world shall be seen,'
As I woke from my dream, cried Napoleon.

JOHN ENGLAND
Hambridge, Somerset

Although **John England** only sang one song that was noted by Cecil Sharp, he is seemingly the singer who had most influence on the course of Sharp's life. For that song, *The Seeds of Love*, was the very first noted down by the great collector and the first in the Sharp canon.

John England worked for Sharp's early collaborator, the Rev. Charles Latimer Marson, who was the perpetual curate of Hambridge in Somerset. John was his gardener, sexton, and also a choir member. Marson had heard John England sing *The Seeds of Love* late in the evening at an annual choir supper, and eventually mentioned him to Sharp as a source of folk songs in the area. Sharp visited Marson in Hambridge and noted the song, which John sang while mowing the Vicarage lawn. The date of that auspicious meeting was 22 August 1903.

Despite 'pumping' John England for more songs, *The Seeds of Love* was the only folk song identified by Sharp, who was not interested in the scores of music hall songs he knew. John had learnt the song while 'turmut hoein' in Dorset' from a man in the adjacent row who made him repeat it until he 'got 'un perfec'. Turnip hoeing is a mind-numbing, back-aching occupation, so teaching each other songs helped pass the time.

The 1901 census records that John England was aged 36, born at Westport, a hamlet of Hambridge, and was living with his wife Rose, also aged 36, born in the next parish of Barrington, and their four children, all born in Hambridge: Joseph Henry C. L. (13), Herbert (10), Kathleen Mary (1) and Albert Edward (1 month).

In the early part of the twentieth century, the newspapers carried many advertisements for emigration to various far-flung destinations of the old Empire. Two of John's sons were tempted and emigrated to Canada. In 1911, having auctioned their furniture and belongings, John and Rose followed them to

North America, where John worked on the sons' farm near Toronto. By 1939 John was reported to be very infirm, suffering from rheumatism, but still able to sing *The Seeds of Love*. It is believed that he died soon afterwards. In 1953, 'Aunt Rose' England wrote from Saskatchewan to her great-nephew in Hambridge proudly claiming that she had 41 grandchildren and great-grandchildren. One of the great-grandchildren later became Bishop of Toronto.

Rose England died in 1957.

Manuscript refs:
FT 1
FW 1
Photo refs: from lantern slide

THE SEEDS OF LOVE

I sowed the seeds of love And I sowed them in the Spring. I ga-ther'd them up in the mor - ning so soon While the small birds do sweet - ly sing While the small birds do sweet-ly sing

I sowed the seeds of love
And I sowed them in the Spring.
I gathered them up in the morning so soon
While the small birds do sweetly sing

My garden was planted well
With flowers everywhere
But I had not the liberty to choose for myself
Of the flowers that I love so dear.

The gardener was standing by
And I asked him to choose for me.
He choosed, for me the Violet, the Lily and
the Pink
But those I refused all three.

The Violet I did not like
Because it bloomed so soon.
The Lily and the Pink, I really overthink,
So I vowed that I'd stay till June.

In June there was a red rose bud,
And that's the flower for me.
I oftentimes have pluck-ed that red rosebud
Till I gained the willow tree.

The willow tree will twist
And the willow tree will twine.
I oftentimes have wished I was in that young
man's arms
That once had the heart of mine.

Come all you false young men,
Do not leave me here to complain,
For the grass that have been oftentimes
trampled under foot
Give it time it will rise up again.

SHADRACH 'SHEPHERD' HAYDEN
Bampton, Oxfordshire

Born in 1829, the son of an agricultural labourer in Lyford, Berkshire, **Shadrach Hayden** (there are various spellings for his name) acquired many fine songs over the course of decades of singing. Moving around an area encompassing the fertile Vale of the White Horse and the northern foothills of the Berkshire Downs, Hayden spent much of his working life labouring on the land. By 1881, he had found regular employment as a shepherd, an occupation which generated the nickname by which he was widely known.

During the 1880s, he relocated to the Thames Valley hamlet of Weald, adjacent to the much larger town of Bampton, where morris dancing has been carried on annually for at least two hundred years. It was Sharp's interest in that morris tradition which led to his first encounter with Hayden, in August 1909, fiddler William 'Jingy' Wells pointing him in his direction. A rapport must have been instantly established, for Sharp visited him on five further occasions during the following three weeks, and again in June 1914, just prior to the outbreak of war and his prolonged stay in America. In all, twenty-seven of his songs were noted for posterity.

Sources for Shadrach's repertory are unknown, but we may observe that he had at least a handful of songs in common with his neighbour of more than a quarter century, Bampton morris dancer and singer Charles 'Cocky' Tanner, who lived only a hundred yards away; while another of Sharp's song informants, Henry Radband, lived in similar proximity. Alfred Williams, collecting in the area some time later, claimed that when it came to repertory, Hayden 'preferred the strong and formal order'. Life mirrored art (he was married to the same woman for more than sixty years), and two years prior

to his death in December 1916, Hayden was, according to Sharp, 'a little deaf [but] in full possession of his faculties and is physically very active'.

Keith Chandler

Manuscript refs:
FT 2289-2291, 2308-2312, 2332-2335, 2365-2371, 2381, 2388-2391, 2431-2433, 2941, 2942
FW 2096-2098, 2103-2111, 2122-2131, 2138-2145, 2157-2164
Photo refs: A58

O ONCE I WAS A SHEPHERD'S BOY

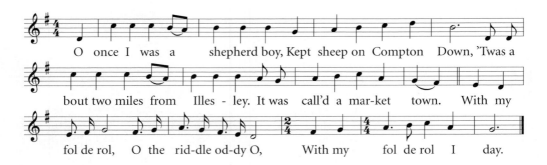

O once I was a shepherd boy, Kept sheep on Compton Down, 'Twas a
bout two miles from Illes - ley. It was call'd a mar-ket town. With my
fol de rol, O the rid-dle od-dy O, With my fol de rol I day.

O once I was a shepherd boy,
Kept sheep on Compton Down,
'Twas about two miles from Illesley.
It was called a market town.

Chorus:
 With my fol de rol, O the riddle oddy O,
 With my fol de rol I day.

And in the morn when we do rise
When daylight do appear
Our breakfast we do get,
To our fold we all do steer.

And when we gets to our sheep fold
We merrily pitched him round
And all the rest part of the day
We sailed the downs all round.

When we gets up on the down
Gazing ourselves all round
We see the storm is rising
And coming on all round.

And the storm is coming on,
The rain fast down do fall,
Neither limb nor tree to shelter me,
I must stand and take it all.

And there we stood in our wet clothes
A-shining and shaking with cold.
We dare not go to shift ourselves
Till we drive our sheep to fold.

And when the storm is over
And that you may plainly see,
I'll never keep sheep on the downs any more,
For there's neither a limb nor a tree.

Bampton Morris with fiddler William 'Jingy' Wells

BETSY HOLLAND
Huntshaw Cross, Devon

In *Walter Raymond, the Man, his Work and Letters* (London: Dent, 1933) Evelyn V. Clark described Cecil Sharp's first meeting with **Betsy Holland**:

During those years Mr. Cecil Sharp went to Withypool with the Rev. F. Etherington, then Rector of Minehead, and Raymond joined them in the search for folk-songs, together with the Rev. Charles L. Marson, Vicar of Hambridge.

On one occasion they had been to Simonsbath to visit an old man with a reputation as a singer of folk-songs. Their journey being unsuccessful … they were returning across the moor, when they fell in with a gipsy camp, and a man and his child outside the tent. Cecil Sharp inquired of the father if he knew any old songs. 'No, but my missus her do', was the reply, as a Romany woman emerged from the tent with her baby. At Cecil Sharp's request she sang a long ballad called The Murder of Macdonald, in which the phrase, 'the cruddle madderer' was often repeated. Mr. Sharp wrote down the tune and Mr. Etherington the words, and on their return to Withypool they set to work to decipher the latter, and were much perplexed at the recurring strange phrase, until it dawned upon the mind of one of the party that the words were 'cruel murderer', extra consonants having been introduced as is the case in dialect speech.

The meeting took place on 20 August 1907, a year after a rift had occurred between Sharp and Marson. If the account is accurate, it may describe an attempt at reconciliation between Sharp and Marson and might have been at the instigation of Etherington, who was a close friend of both men. It would appear that they were based at Walter Raymond's cottage in Withypool, which subsequently became Etherington's parish.

Sharp continues the story in *Folk Songs from Somerset (Series Five)*:

Mrs. Betsy Holland is a gipsy woman … She is one of the finest folk-singers I have ever come across, and I shall not readily forget the impression which her singing of this song made upon me.

The melody is in the Lydian mode, the only folk tune in that mode that, so far as I am aware, has yet been recovered in England. To make certain that I had noted it correctly, I followed Mrs. Holland, a few days afterwards, to Huntshaw Cross in N. Devon, and asked her to sing the song once again. She repeated it exactly as I had taken it

down at Simonsbath. As she told me that she had learned the song from her grandmother, I then went in pursuit of the latter, whom I eventually found near Honiton. Mrs. Rebecca Holland had nearly forgotten the song, but she was able to sing enough of it for me to hear the F-sharp, the distinctive note of the mode.

... Mrs. Holland varied her tune a great deal in different verses, and often in a way which it was impossible to note down accurately on paper. I hope some day to get a record of the song on the phonograph.

The meeting at Huntshaw Cross took place on 25 August 1907, and Sharp noted three more songs from Betsy, whom he also noted

was 26 at the time. The search for Rebecca Holland lasted until 2 September and involved enquiries with the police authorities. The excitement of finding a Lydian tune is almost palpable.

Sharp and Etherington met Betsy Holland again about a year later, on the Quantock Hills in Somerset when no songs were recorded. Etherington marvelled at the likeness of Betsy Holland's son and his own.

Manuscript refs:
FT 1428, 1443-1445
FW 1311-1313, 1328-1330
Photo refs: A20

RIGGS O' LONDON TOWN

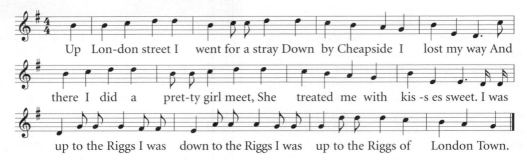

Up London street I went for a stray
Down by Cheapside I lost my way
And there I did a pretty girl meet,
She treated me with kisses sweet.
  I was up to the Riggs
  I was down to the Riggs
  I was up to the Riggs of London Town.

She took me to a house of fame
And there she axed me my name.
Aloud for supper she did call
A-thinking love would pay for all.

This supper being over and table cleared
She called for wine my heart to cheer.
She called for wine both white and red
And the chambermaid for to make the bed.

'Twixt the hours of ten and eleven
My love she axed me to bed to come,
For I said silence gives consent
To my love's chamber bed I went.

'Twixt the hour of two and three
Out of the bed I gently crept
And milled her pocket and there I found
A silver snuff box and ten pound.

As flats and sharps wherever you be
If you meet a pretty girl be kind and free
[Pray use her well whatever may betide]
And remember me by Cheapside.

LOUIE HOOPER
Hambridge, Somerset

The third song in the Sharp collection was contributed by **Louie Hooper** and her sister (possibly half-sister) Lucy White, noted down in late August 1903. Between that time and April 1906, Sharp noted a hundred songs from the two sisters, out of an estimated repertoire of three hundred songs. Most of the songs were either learnt from their mother, Sarah England, who was known for her singing locally, or while working together as shirt-makers. So, not surprisingly, their repertoires were similar. Also unsurprisingly, they were main contributors to *Folk Songs from Somerset*, and, had the rift between Sharp and Marson in 1906 not curtailed Sharp's collecting in Hambridge, their contribution might have been greater.

In the 1901 census Louisa Hooper, a 40 year old widow, is given as the head of a household at Westport near Hambridge, living with a daughter Flossie, aged 15, and a son, Archie, aged 8 (Bertie, Archie's twin, had died in infancy). According to the parish register, she had been widowed a month after her wedding in 1884. She had also been disabled from an early age, if not from birth, spending more time with her mother and other adults than most of the local children, which provided opportunities for her to learn more of their songs than her sister. She had always been very musical and recalled lying in bed as a child putting words to the rhythm of the rain on the roof. Although there were periods when she could not attend school, she received enough education to write a letter to A. H. Fox Strangways in 1931 after he had made an appeal in the local press for people who had known Sharp to contact him.

In the early years of the twentieth century there was an extensive network of 'out-working' in south Somerset, particularly in the gloving, withy-stripping and shirt-making trades. The proprietor of the business provided the equipment and materials and collected the completed articles once a week. At Westport the women used to gather in one of the houses to work together, singing and chatting while they worked. Thus Louie and Lucy learnt many songs.

One aspect of Sharp's time in Hambridge that is rarely mentioned is the fun and excitement that he and the singers experienced together. When she recalled another song Louie Hooper tells how 'he would be dizzy until he had written it down'. Sharp took Louie Hooper to Ilminster Fair on 30 August 1905 'to hear the old people sing' and smoked a piece of glass so that she could look at the eclipse of the sun. He gave her a copy of *Folk Songs from Somerset*, on the basis that 'fair exchange is no robbery'. It was not unknown for him to give presents to his singers: these included a concertina for Louie and tobacco for the men, while Mrs Sharp gave Louie and Lucy a blouse each. He was also known to pay his singers 'very well'. He took Lucy and Louie to a concert of his collected songs in Langport and showed a photograph of Louie's Christmas dinner in a lantern lecture, while she was in the audience.

Sometimes there were high jinks at Hambridge Vicarage, especially if Mrs Marson was away, with forays into the pantry for a scratch meal and Sharp appearing with a bag of doughnuts he called 'Sudden Death'. On one occasion Emma Overd, Louie Hooper, Lucy White, Sarah Hutchings and Liza Hutchings dressed in bonnets and shawls that they had borrowed and Sharp took a photograph of them. As Louie wrote to Fox Strangways: '… I Louie Hooper and my sister Lucy White … spent many a happy hour singing to him at the Vicarage Hambridge … I liked him (Sharp) very much … It was a happy time.'

In 1942 there was great excitement in Westport when a BBC van parked outside Louie's cottage for the purpose of recording some of her songs. Subsequently they were broadcast on the World Service and a listener in New Zealand was so taken by them that he sent a tin of jam to Louie, care of the BBC. It remained on a shelf at the BBC until the broadcast was repeated and someone finally realised who the recipient was supposed to be and the tin was forwarded to Westport.

Louie Hooper died in 1946 and is buried in Hambridge churchyard.

Manuscript refs:
FT 5, 49, 55, 88-90, 101-103, 132-139, 191, 192, 196, 265, 319, 320, 322, 324-326
FW 10, 75, 83, 84, 91,94, 97, 98, 100, 110, 111, 207-212, 283-286, 288, 289, 291, 292, 432, 433, 445, 446, 448-450, 899, 900
Photo refs: B9
Corresp: Box 4/folder a/item 8

With Lucy White:
Manuscript refs:
FT 3, 6-12, 14-16, 19-21, 24-27, 34, 38, 39, 50-54, 63-66, 77-79
FW 3-5, 11-22, 25-27, 31-35, 41-46, 63, 64, 69-71, 81, 82, 85-90, 92, 93, 105, 286

THE FOGGY DEW

One night as I lay on my bed,
As I lay fast asleep,
A pretty maid came to my bedside
Most bitterly she did weep.

She wrung her hands and tore her hair,
Crying, asking: 'What shall I do?'
'Go home to bed, my fair pretty maid,
For fear of the foggy dew, dew, dew,
For fear of the foggy dew.'

So there they laid all that long night
Till daylight did appear.
'Come rise, pretty maid, and don't be afraid
For the foggy dew, is gone, gone, gone.
For the foggy dew is gone.'

I never told her all her faults
And I never do intend so to do,
But there's many a time I've rolled her in my arms
For fear of the foggy dew, dew, dew,
For fear of the foggy dew.

HERE'S TO MY TIN

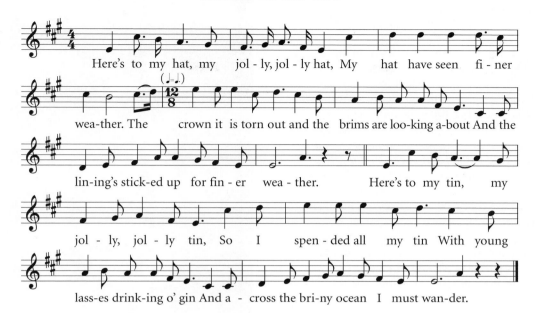

Here's to my hat, my jolly, jolly hat,
My hat have seen finer weather.
The crown it is torn out and the brims are
looking about
And the lining's sticked up for finer weather.

Chorus
Here's to my tin, my jolly, jolly tin,
So I spended all my tin
With young lasses drinking o' gin
And across the briny ocean I must wander.

Here's to my jacket, my jolly, jolly jacket,
My jacket have seen better weather,
The back it is torn out and the sleeves they
are weared out
And the collar's sticked up for finer weather.

Here's to my waistcoat, my jolly, jolly
waistcoat,
My waistcoat have seen finer weather,
The back it is weared out and the fronts are
looking about
And the pockets are sticked up for finer
weather.

Here's to my shirt, my jolly, jolly shirt,
My shirt have seen better weather,
The tail it is torn out and the sleeves are
looking about
And the collar's sticked up for finer weather.

Here's to my stockings, my jolly, jolly
stockings,
My stockings have seen better weather,
The toes they are weared out and the heels
are looking about
And the uppers are sticking up for finer
weather.

Here's to my shoes, my jolly, jolly shoes,
My shoes have seen better weather,
The bottoms they are weared out and the uppers
are looking about
And the tongue's sticked up for finer weather.

ELIZABETH LOCK
Muchelney Ham, Somerset

Mrs Elizabeth Lock was living at Muchelney Ham with her husband, George, a tenant farmer, when Cecil Sharp came to call. Between April 1904 and September 1905, she provided Sharp with over twenty songs, two of which were included in *Folk Songs from Somerset*: *Hares on the Mountain* and *High Germany*. Extracts from others were included within some of the other songs published.

At the time of the 1901 census, Elizabeth was 60 and George 62, both having been born in Muchelney. Elizabeth fell and broke her thigh while going into church in March 1915, and died two months later. Dr R. P. Hosford reported that she was suffering from 'senile decay' and that her arteries were brittle.

Manuscript refs:
FT 159-164, 185-188, 253-259, 452-454, 498, 546, 645
FW 243-249, 273-276, 351, 352, 361-365, 615, 714
Photo refs: B16

GROUND FOR THE FLOOR

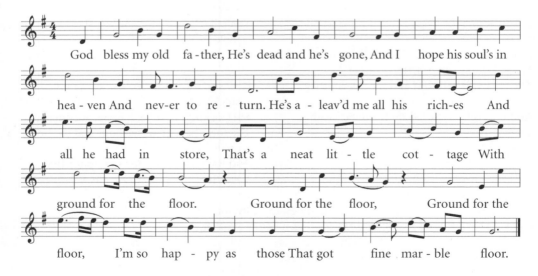

God bless my old fa-ther, He's dead and he's gone, And I hope his soul's in hea-ven And nev-er to re-turn. He's a-leav'd me all his rich-es And all he had in store, That's a neat lit-tle cot-tage With ground for the floor. Ground for the floor, Ground for the floor, I'm so hap-py as those That got fine mar-ble floor.

God bless my old father,
He's dead and he's gone,
And I hope his soul's in heaven
And never to return.
He's a-leaved me all his riches
And all he had in store,
That's a neat little cottage
With ground for the floor.

As for grates I've got none
But my fire's on the ground.
As for chairs I've got none
To set myself down
I've a three legged stool
That's the chiefest of my store.
If you look underneath
You'll find ground for the floor.

    Ground for the floor,
    Ground for the floor,
    I'm so happy as those
    That got fine marble floor.

    Ground for the floor.
    Ground for the floor,
    I'm so happy as those
    That got thousands in store.

    My cottage is surrounded
    With brambles and thorns
    And so sweet are the notes
    Of the birds in the morn.
    [I've a guinea in my pocket
    And plenty more in store
    If you look down below
    You'll find ground for the floor.]

FROM RICHES TO POVERTY or ADIEU TO OLD ENGLAND ADIEU

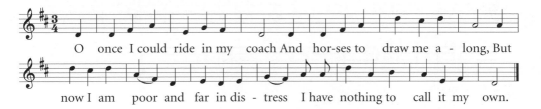

O once I could ride in my coach
And horses to draw me along,
But now I am poor and far in distress
I have nothing to call it my own.

Chorus
    Adieu to old England, adieu,
    Adieu to some hundreds of pounds,
    If the world had been ended O when I was
       young
    My sorrows I never should have known.

O once I could eat the best bread
And the bread that was made of best wheat,
But now I am glad of that dry moulded crust
And glad I have got it to eat.

O once I could lay on a bed
And a bed that was made of fine down
But now I am glad of a lock of clean straw
To lay this poor body down on.

    O once I could drink the best beer
    And the beer that was made of fine brown.
    But now I am glad of a drop of cold water
    That runs from town to town.

THOMAS MITCHELL
Merriott, Somerset

In 1901, **Thomas Clark Mitchell** was a 28 year old farmer, unmarried and living with his parents, William Clark Mitchell and Louisa Mitchell. Two sisters, Emily Clark Mitchell (34) and Loie (*sic*) Clark Mitchell (25), plus a brother, Ben Clark Mitchell (30), were also in the household.

On 25 August 1905, Sharp collected *The Painful Plough* from Thomas and returned nine days later to confirm his notes. The reason for the second visit becomes clear from the notes in *Folk Songs from Somerset (Series Two)*:

It is a noble melody but at the same time a very curious one, and it has puzzled me not a little. For, the seventh note, which occurs but once in the course of the melody, and that near its close, is major; yet the air is nevertheless, in my opinion, in the Mixolydian mode. I have, accordingly, so harmonised it; but I am quite prepared to find some expert musicians disagree with me.

The Painful Plough was the only song that Sharp noted.

Manuscript refs:
FT 599
FW 689-691
Photo refs: none

The Painful Plough – from Sharp's field notebook

THE PAINFUL PLOUGH

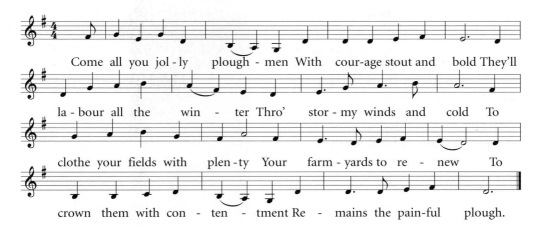

Come all you jol-ly plough-men With cour-age stout and bold They'll
la-bour all the win - ter Thro' stor-my winds and cold To
clothe your fields with plen-ty Your farm-yards to re - new To
crown them with con - ten - tment Re - mains the pain-ful plough.

Come all you jolly ploughmen
With courage stout and bold
They'll labour all the winter
Thro' stormy winds and cold
To clothe your fields with plenty
Your farmyards to renew
To crown them with contentment
Remains the painful plough.

Adam was a ploughman
When ploughing first began,
The next that did succeed him
Was Cain his eldest son.
Some of their generation
Their calling doth pursue
That bread may not be wanted
Remains the painful plough.

O ploughman, says the gardener,
Don't count your trade with ours.
There's walking in the garden
To view those early flowers.
There's all those curious borders
And pleasant walks to view,
There's no such peace and contentment
Provided by the plough.

O gardener, says the ploughman,
Our calling don't despise.
Every man for his living
Doth on his trade relies.
Were it not for the ploughman
Both rich and poor must rue
For we're all depending
Upon the painful plough.

Behold the wealthy merchants
That trades upon the seas
That brings the golden treasures
To those that live at ease,
That brings the fruit and spices
And silks too also
They are brought from the Indies
By virtue of the plough.

And the men that do bring them,
We've only to be true
They could not sail the ocean
Without the painful plough.
For they must have bread biscuits
Flour, pudding, beef and peas
To feed the jolly sailors
As they sail upon the seas.

I hope no one's offended
With me for singing this
For I never was intended
For anything amiss.
If you consider it rightly
You'll find what I say is true
Not a man that you can mention
Can live without the plough.

Thomas Mitchell 59

ELIZABETH MOGG
Doddington and Holford, Somerset

Elizabeth Mogg, generally known as Granny Mogg, lived at Doddington, Somerset, prior to moving to a single room at Holford towards the end of her life. In her final years, when she was effectively bedridden, she kept a stick laid across her bed with which she threatened the village children when they teased and tormented her. Sharp noted that she had two illegitimate sons and consumed prodigious amounts of snuff. He collected eight songs from her on two visits during 1904 and 1906.

According to the 1901 census, the only Elizabeth Mogg living in the district was in Taunton, as a lodger with her niece Emma Williams and her great-niece Amy Williams.

Elizabeth Mogg died at Holford in 1921, aged 91.

Manuscript refs:
FT 373–378, 984, 985
FW 502–507, 1027
Photo refs: A5

Banks of Green Willow – from Sharp's field notebook

BANKS OF GREEN WILLOW

It's of a sea cap-tain Down by the sea - side O, He court - ed a young dam - sel And got her by child.

It's of a sea captain
Down by the sea-side O,
He courted a young damsel
And got her by child.

'Go and get your mother's will O
And all your father's money
To sail across the ocean
Along with your Johnny.'

'I've got my father's will O
And all my mother's money
To sail across the ocean
Along with my Johnny.'

We had not sailed miles,
No not great many,
Before she was delivered
Of a beautiful baby.

'Go and get me a white napkin
To tie my head easy
To throw me quite overboard
Both me and my baby.'

Now see how she totters,
Now see how she tumbers,
Now see how she's rolling
All on the salt water.

'Go and get me a long boat
To row my love back again,
To row my love back again,
Both she and her baby.'

Now she shall have a coffin,
A coffin shall shine yellow,
And she shall be buried
On the banks of Green Willow.

The bells shall ring mournful
O for my dearest Polly
And she shall be buried
For the sake of her money.

CHARLES NEVILLE
East Coker, Somerset

Charles Neville of East Coker sang for Cecil Sharp on 2 and 3 September 1908, during which visits a total of fourteen songs were noted. Charles' son, Alfred, was on hand to help out with a rendering of *The Barley Mow*. As Sharp observed: 'When Mr. Neville sang it to me the chorus was sustained by his son, whom I helped as well as I could.' It was Alfred who introduced his father to Sharp, having given him two songs on a previous occasion.

Three of Charles' songs were included in *Folk Songs from Somerset (Series Five)*: *The Barley Mow*, *My Man John* (in which Sharp substituted an alternative final verse as Charles' 'would scarcely bear reproduction')

and a tune to *The Green Wedding*.

In the last, 'Mr. Neville sang this air to a ballad called "*The Boatsman and the Tailor*", the words of which were too boisterous and free to reproduce here.'

In the 1901 census, Charles Neville is listed as a 51 year old woodman, widowed, and living with five unmarried children, Gilbert (25), Effie (23), Martha (19), William (18) and Alfred (15), and his mother-in-law, Emma Young, aged 89. All of them had been born in East Coker. The two oldest sons were web weavers, while Alfred was a twine maker. No occupations were given for the women.

Manuscript refs:
FT 1817-1824, 1834-1836, 1839, 1840
FW 1666-1675, 1677-1679
Photo refs:

The Boatsman and the Tailor– from Sharp's field notebook

JOHN BARLEYCORN

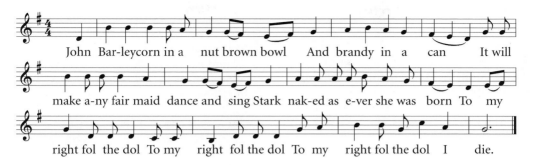

John Bar-leycorn in a nut brown bowl And brandy in a can It will make a-ny fair maid dance and sing Stark nak-ed as e-ver she was born To my right fol the dol To my right fol the dol To my right fol the dol I die.

John Barleycorn in a nut brown bowl
And brandy in a can
It will make any fair maid dance and sing
Stark naked as ever she was born
  To my right fol the dol
  To my right fol the dol
  To my right fol the dol I die.

Alternative text from John Trump of North Petherton, Somerset

There was three men came out of the North,
They all do swear and say,
They gently made a solemn oath,
That Barleycorn should die.

Chorus:
  With my right fol i dol i day.

Then the seedsman he comes on
And spread him over the land,
The next the ploughman did begin,
To throw clods upon his head.

Then they did rejoice and sing
That Barleycorn was dead,
There he lie a-sleeping,
Till rain from sky it falls.

Then up jumped John Barleycorn,
Made them liars all,
There he grew till harvest,
Till he was pale and wan,
Then he grew till he had a beard,
Long as any man's.

The harvest men with the scythes so sharp,
They cut him off from beneath,
They dashed his head against the ground,
They served him bitterly.

The harvest men with their forks so sharp,
They prick him to his heart,
The next they served him worse than that,
They tied him to some cart.

They whirled him round and round,
Till they got him to some barn,
And then they made a mow of him,
Not thinking any harm.

The next the thresher he comes in,
And beat his skin from bone,
And the old miller served him the worst of all,
He ground him between two stones.

Put red wine in a bottle,
And can it in a can,
Put old Sir John in another fine bowl,
And you'll pull down the strongest man.

The huntsman he came out one day,
Did loudly blow his horn,
And all the people did rejoice and sing,
For the sake of Barleycorn.

WILLIAM NOTT
Meshaw, Devon

Cecil Sharp visited **William Nott** of Meshaw, Devon, on six occasions within the twelve months beginning January 1904. He contributed a total of thirty-one songs to the collection, several of a humorous nature, such as *The Thrashing Machine* and *The Little Cobbler and the Butcher*, but mostly what would have been considered standard folk songs, including the Child ballad, *Barbara Allen*. In visiting six times it is obvious that Sharp held a very high opinion of William's repertoire and singing.

It has been suggested that William Nott was a tenant farmer, in which case he is probably the William Nott who was at Pittford Farm, Winkleigh, in the 1901 census, living with a wife, a daughter, two servants and a boarder.

Manuscript refs:
FT 82-85, 93-99, 115, 118, 120-123, 432-439, 476-481
FW 137, 141-144, 147-152, 159-166, 189-198, 551-554, 578-581
Photo refs: B6

THE DARK EYED SAILOR

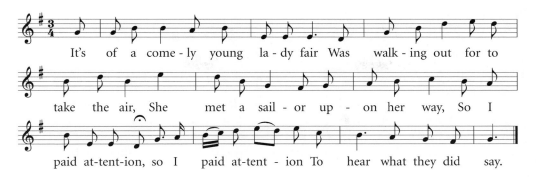

It's of a come-ly young la-dy fair Was walk-ing out for to take the air, She met a sail-or up-on her way, So I paid at-tent-ion, so I paid at-tent-ion To hear what they did say.

[It's] of a comely young lady fair
Was walking out for to take the air,
She met a sailor upon her way,
So I paid attention, so I paid attention
To hear what they did say.

Said William: 'Lady, why rove alone,
The night is come and the day's near gone.'
She said, while tears from her eyes did fall:
''Tis the dark eyed sailor, 'tis the dark eyed
    sailor
That's proven my downfall.

It's two long years since he left the land,
I took the gold ring from off my hand.
We broke the token, here's a part with me.
And the other rolling, the other rolling
In the bottom of the sea.'

Said William: 'Drive him off from your mind,
Some other sailor as good you'll find.
[Love] turns aside and soon cold doth grow
Like the winter's morning, like the winter's
    morning
When the lands are clothed with snow.'

These words did Phoebe's fond heart inflame.
She says: 'On me you shall play no game.'
She drew a dagger and then she did cry,
'For my dark eyed sailor, for my dark eyed
    sailor
A maid I'll live and die.

With his coal-black eyes and curly hair
His pleasing tongue did my heart ensnare.
Gently he was but no wretch like you
To advise a maiden, to advise a maiden
To slight the jacket blue.'

'But still,' said Phoebe, 'I'll never disdain
A tarry sailor, but treat the same
So drink his health, here's a piece of coin,
But the dark-eyed sailor, the dark-eyed sailor
Still claims this heart of mine.'

Then half the ring did young William show.
She seems distracted midst joy and woe.
'No welcome, I've lands and gold
For my dark-eyed sailor, for my dark-eyed
    sailor
So [manly] true and bold.'

There in a village down by the sea.
They joined in wedlock and well agree.
So maids be true while your love's away.
For a cloudy morning, for a cloudy morning
Brought forth the pleasant day.

JACK THE JOLLY TAR

Oh I am Jack and a jol-ly tar O Let me re-turn from the sea so far O Oh I am Jack and a jo-lly tar Let me return from the sea so far. Fal la la doo Fal lal le-ro Right fal la la doo.

Oh I am Jack and a jolly tar O
Let me return from the sea so far O
Oh I am Jack and a jolly tar
Let me return from the sea so far.
   Fal la la doo
   Fal lal lero
   Right fal la la doo.

As I was walking through London city
I found myself all in great pity,
For I heard them say as I passed by:
Poor Jack all in the streets must lie.

The Squire courted for his fancy
A merchant's daughter whose name was
   Nancy.
And I heard them agree as I passed by
That night together for to lie.

'Oh tie a string unto your finger
And let it hang unto the window,
And I will come and touch the string
And you come down and let me in.'

'Blame me,' said Jack, 'if I don't venture,
I'll touch the string that hangs to the
   window.'
And Jack he went and touched the string,
And she came down and let Jack in.

Next morning soon as she was wakened
She looked like one that was forsaken
For to see Jack lie with his check shirt
And almost covered all over in dirt.

'Oh then,' said she, 'how came you here O?
I'm afraid you've robbed me of my Squire O.'
'No, no,' said Jack, 'I touched the string
And you came down and let me in.'

'While it is so it makes no matter
For Jack's the lad I'll follow after.
For I do love Jack as I love my life
And I do intend to be Jack's wife.'

The Squire come all in a passion.
Saying: 'Curse the women through the nation,
For there is not one that will prove true
And if there is 'tis very few.'

EMMA OVERD
Langport, Somerset

Mrs Emma Overd, generally known as Mary, was the most extrovert singer that Sharp encountered in Somerset. His account of their first meeting is worth retelling:

He was told an amusing story of an encounter with a woman who had a great reputation as a singer. She lived in a mean street, which was inhabited – so he was told – by 'bad people'. She was out when he first called upon her, but was said to be at the public-house round the corner. As he approached the public-house he saw a group of women standing outside and chatting. 'Is Mrs. Overd here' he asked. 'That's my name,' an elderly woman replied, 'and what do you want of me?' Cecil Sharp explained that he was hunting for old songs and hoped that she would sing him some; whereupon without any warning she flung her arms around his waist and danced him round and round with the utmost vigour, shouting 'Lor, girls, here's my beau at last.' In the middle of this terpsichorean display Cecil Sharp heard a shocked exclamation, 'But surely that is Mr Sharp,' and looking round he saw the vicar, with whom he was staying, and the vicar's daughter, both gazing with horror on the scene. When asked what he did, Sharp said: 'Oh, I shouted to them to go away – and they went.'

(*Cecil Sharp: His Life and Work*, by Maud Karpeles, London: RKP, 1967)

The 'mean street' was Knapps Lane, Langport, between the railway and the River Parrett. At one end of a row of four cottages lived Emma Overd and her husband William, a labourer, and at the other end lived Eliza Hutchings. In two cottages between them lived Eliza Hutchings' daughter, Ellen Trott, and her husband Edward and their eleven children. Eliza Hutchings and Ellen Trott both supplied songs to Cecil Sharp.

Mrs Overd was 67 when she first met Sharp, describing herself as having had nine children, six living and being all married. Her singing style was described by Sharp as being with great 'dramatic fervour', and in a review of one of his lectures it was noted of Emma's rendition of *Bruton Town* that:

. . . the good lady rose about the end of the third verse, when the unfortunate murdered lover appears in a dream to his beloved, and declaimed the rest of the tragedy in melodramatic style, thumping the table in her excitement.

Knapps Lane

Elsewhere Sharp has described how Emma Overd and Eliza Hutchings sang and danced together while performing *Dicky of Taunton Deane*, 'in a way that I shall not easily forget', and Emma refreshed herself with a 'moog of cider'.

Emma Overd was one of the few singers to sing the scatological *Crabfish* to Sharp, the text of which had to be rewritten by Charles Marson for publication. Sharp commented:

Mrs Overd sang her song very excitedly and at break-neck speed, punctuating the rhythm of the refrain with lusty blows of her fists on the table.

From Sharp's comments it is obvious that his affection for her stretched well beyond the forty-three songs that she supplied over at least eleven visits in five years, nine of which appeared in *Folk Songs from Somerset.*

The 1901 census gives Emma Overd's age as 63, while George was 65 and the last son at home, Arthur, 24. Both George and Arthur are listed as 'Ordinary Agricultural Labourers'. Emma and George Overd were both born at Curry Rivel, and Sharp's first visit to her was the day following a visit to Harry Richards at that very place.

Emma Overd died in 1928.

Manuscript refs:
FT 240, 241, 245-248, 262-264, 292-297, 308-314, 327, 328, 330-332, 341-343, 346, 379-381, 440-443, 2030-2033, 2035
FW 332-334, 342-347, 371-374, 394-402, 417-429, 453-460, 469-471, 473, 474, 508-510, 555-560, 878, 1902-1904, 1907
Photo refs: B19

KING GEORGE

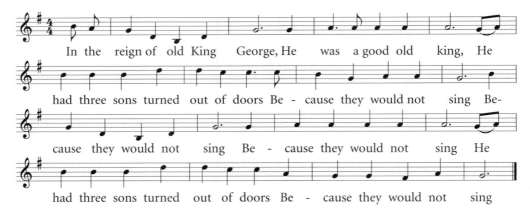

In the reign of old King George, He was a good old king, He had three sons turned out of doors Be-cause they would not sing Be-cause they would not sing Be-cause they would not sing He had three sons turned out of doors Be-cause they would not sing

In the reign of old King George,
He was a good old king,
He had three sons turned out of doors
Because they would not sing
  Because they would not sing
  Because they would not sing
  He had three sons turned out of doors
  Because they would not sing

The first he was a miller,
The next he was a weaver
And the third he was a proud tailor
And it's three bad rogues together (etc.)

The miller he stole corn,
And the weaver he stole yarn,
And the tailor he stole broadcloth
For to keep the three rogues warm (etc.)

So the miller was drowned in his pond,
And the weaver was hanged in his yarn,
And the devil carried away the proud tailor
With the broadcloth under his arm (etc.)

I WISH I HAD NEVER KNOWN

I wish I had never known no man at all
Since love has been a grief and proved my downfall,
Since love has been a grief and a tyrant to me,
I lost my love fighting for sweet liberty.

I wish I had never seen his curled hair
And neither that I'd been in his company there.
'Twas his red rosy cheeks, his dark rolling eye
And his flattering tongue caused my poor heart to sigh.

People came to me and thus they did say:
Your lover has gone, has gone far away.
But if ever he return I will crown him with joy
I fly to the arms of my dear darling boy.

If I had wings like an eagle I'd fly,
I'd fly to the arms of my dear darling boy,
And on his soft bosom I'd build up my nest,
I'd lay my head down on his white snowy breast.

Some say I'm with child, but that I'll deny,
Some say I'm with child, but I'll prove it a lie.
I'll tarry awhile and soon let them know
That he likes me too well to serve me so.

Some do wear spencers and I don't wear none,
And they that don't like me can leave me alone.
He'll have me or leave me and so let me go
For I don't care a straw if he have me or no.

ROBERT PARISH
Exford, Somerset

Robert Parish of Exford was second in a line of three generations of Parishs who served as sextons in the village for a period spanning over a hundred years. Sharp noted that he 'was sarving (sic) in Plymouth in '49 when the cholera (struck)' and that a Mr J. Parish of Cremyll Street, Stonehouse, Plymouth 'knows all words but <u>no</u> tunes'. Whether or not Mr J. Parish was a relative is not known.

Robert (or Bob as he was also known) was born in Exford in 1823 and married Jane Quartley of the adjacent parish, Cutcombe, in 1844. They had three daughters and three sons, the youngest of whom, also a Bob, followed in his father's footsteps as sexton, singer and storyteller. Robert senior was known as a 'dear old man', a quiet man and a man of principle.

In the course of six visits during 1906 and 1907, Sharp noted twenty-two songs from Robert. Three of them were used in *Folk Songs from Somerset*. In his immediate community, however, he was not generally considered as a musical person and his name does not occur in connection with the village band or the carol party, which was particularly strong.

Although listed in the 1901 census return as an agricultural labourer at the age of 78, in his latter years as sexton his duties included ringing the passing bell, grave digging and acting as an odd job man at the rectory. Indeed, he lived in Ivy Cottage, which was part of the church glebe.

In July 1909 the passing bell was tolled for Robert, aged 87, and a headstone cut for him by his son, Bob, which has subsequently disappeared.

Manuscript refs:
FT 1117-1120, 1123-1127, 1418-1427, 1430, 1431, 1453
FW 1108-1124, 1304-1310, 1314, 1332
Photo refs: A24

FAREWELL LADS AND LASSES

Fare-well my lads and fare-well my lasses, Now I think I've got-ten my choice.
I will go a-way to yon-der moun-tains Where I thought I heard his voice.
Where he hol-loa, I will fol-low Round the world that is so wide.
For young Tho-mas he did me promise I would be his law-ful bride.

Farewell my lads and farewell my lasses,
Now I think I've gotten my choice.
I will go away to yonder mountains
Where I thought I heard his voice.
Where he holloa, I will follow
Round the world that is so wide.
For young Thomas he did me promise
I would be his lawful bride.

Singing sweetly and completely
Songs of pleasure and of love
My heart is with you altogether
Though I live not where I love.

Alternative text from Robert Barrett of Dorset

I LIVE NOT WHERE I LOVE

Come all you maids that live at a distance
Many a mile from off your swain,
Come and assist me this very moment
For to pass away some time,
Singing sweetly and completely
Songs of pleasure and of love
My heart is with you altogether
Though I live not where I love.

O when I sleeps I dreams about you
When I wake I take no rest,
For every instant thinking on you
My heart e'er fixed in your breast,
O this cold absence seems at a distance
And many a mile from my true love
But my heart is with her altogether
Though I live not where I love.

So farewell lads and farewell lasses,
Now I think I've got my choice,
I will away to yonder mountains
Where I think I hear his voice.
And if he holloa I will follow
Around the world that is so wide,
For young Thomas he did promise
I shall be his lawful bride.

Now if the world was of one religion,
Every living thing would die,
Or if I prove false unto my jewel
Or any way my love deny,
The world shall change and be most strange
If ever I my mind remove.
My heart is with her altogether
Though I live not where I love.

VAN DIEMAN'S LAND

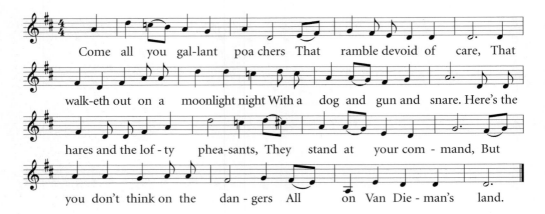

Come all you gal-lant poa chers That ramble devoid of care, That
walk-eth out on a moonlight night With a dog and gun and snare. Here's the
hares and the lof - ty phea-sants, They stand at your com - mand, But
you don't think on the dan - gers All on Van Die - man's land.

Come all you gallant poachers
That ramble devoid of care,
That walketh out on a moonlight night
With a dog and gun and snare.
Here's the hares and the lofty pheasants,
They stand at your command,
But you don't think on the dangers
All on Van Dieman's land.

Here's poor Tom Brown from Nottingham,
Jack Williams and poor Joe,
They was three of the daring poachers
The country did well know.
One night they was trap-handed
By the keepers hid in sand
And for fourteen years transported
All on Van Dieman's land.

The very first day we landed
All on that fatal shore
The planters they came round us
About three score or more;
So they harnessed us up like horses
And fit us out of hand
And they yoked us to the plough, my boys,
To plough Van Dieman's land.

O those wretched huts that we live in
Is built with clods and clay
And rotten straw for bedding
We dare not say Nay.
Our cottages they're all fenced with fire
We slumber whilst we can
To drive all wolf and tiger
All from Van Dieman's Land.

One night all in my slumbers
I had a pleasant dream.
I dreamed I was with my dear wife
Down by some purling stream.
With the children's prattling stories
All around me they did stand;
But I awoke quite broken hearted
All on Van Dieman's land.

Here is a girl from Nottingham,
Susan Somers is her name,
She got fourteen years transported
For selling of our game.
But the planter's bought her freedom
And married her out of hand
And she proved true and kind to us
All on Van Dieman's land.

JAMES PROLE
Monksilver, Somerset

In 1901, **James Prole** (not Proll, as noted by Sharp) was listed in the census return as a millwright, aged 55, living in Watchet. With him lived his wife Mary, also 55, two single sons, Ernest and Robert (respectively 24 and 18, both employees at a paper mill), a daughter, Ada (16 and a school teacher), and a grandson, Ronald Prole, aged 2 years. Jim's occupation would have attracted plenty of opportunities in the area, what with a paper mill operating in Watchet and many small water mills on the fast flowing streams running off the Brendon Hills and Exmoor.

Sharp noted seven songs from Jim, whom he met in Monksilver on 10 September 1906. *Sweet Lovely Joan* was used in *Folk Songs from Somerset (Series Four)*. The photograph shows that it was a sunny day when Sharp came to visit and his shadow is clearly visible as he takes the picture.

Manuscript refs:
FT 1135-1141
FW 1128-1130
Photo refs: A2

Come All Brother Seamen – from Sharp's field notebook

COME ALL BROTHER SEAMEN

Come all brother seamen come listen a while
I'll sing you a story, 'twill cause you to smile
Concerning a story to you I will tell
There's misfortunes will happen, 'tis all very
  well.

I had my discharge, I had gold in store
I'll tell you by and by how I came by some
  more
I being half tight to an ale house went in
To dance and to caper, I then did begin.

There were ladies in splendour in the height
  of their glee
Thought I to myself one is for me
There was one really rigged in a long black
  silk gown
I gave her the wink and she by me sat down.

I called in the waiter to bring in some gin
She said 'That's all right Jack that is just the
  thing
If you're the lad that will lodgings provide
It's I am the girl that'll lie by your side.'

[All things being agreed between doxy and I]
I called in the waiter to know what's to pay
Ten shilling and sixpence the waiter replied
I paid down the money and upstairs went I.

I quickly unrigged and jumped into bed
And placed my shatlock [shot locker] under
  my head
Pretty Betsy and I wished each other good
  night
We fell fast asleep as she thought herself
  right.

But twelve in the night, Pretty Betsy arose
And all her intent was to find out my clothes
But very well it was I knew her intent
And all her whole search was to find out my
  rent.

I jumped out of bed, I followed by blows
I gave her no time for to put on her clothes
Till the clothes she had on her in ribbons did
  fly
Crying 'Ten thousand murders, Lord, what
  shall I do?'

I quickly went back to see what I could find
As poor girl in her fright left her pocket
  behind
There was ten guineas and two five pound
  notes
Her long black silk gown, her silk stockings
  and clothes.

So now brother comrade, I've ended my song
I hope brother comrade I've done nothing wrong
So fill up your glasses and drink my health round
I hope you'll serve every girl the same turn.

HARRY RICHARDS
Curry Rivel, Somerset

Harry Richards was actually Henry Richards, but universally known as 'Harry', as often happened. However, as Henry had a brother named Harry, the situation becomes rather confusing.

For most of his working life, Harry, the singer, was a 'stonequarryman', but in later life became an odd-job man, or 'strapper', paid at a daily rate. By the standards of the day, he was a big man at 6' 3" tall and well built. According to Sharp, he had a bass voice and may have sung in a choir at some time in his life. Sharp noted how he managed octave jumps in *The Trees They Do Grow High* and how he varied the ending of each verse.

Harry was a strict father and a very religious man, and, at least in his latter days, had a sharp tongue, with observations directed at visitors such as, 'Haven't people got anything to do in their own homes?' When his wife Eleanor died, who had been a seamstress and ran a small sweet shop, he insisted that his son and daughter-in-law and their family move in with him. The daughter-in-law was not at all pleased. Every evening Harry would pray for an hour, kneeling on cold linoleum, and, when an old man, one granddaughter would be asked to read the Bible to him each Sunday evening, while another would take him to the Church of England service on Sunday mornings. He believed that picking up a stick for the fire on a Sunday was a sin.

Harry sang 20 songs for Sharp between 1904 and 1909, and one granddaughter recalled being told to be quiet when Sharp returned a few years later. Four of the songs appeared in *Folk Songs from Somerset*: *The Trees They Do Grow High, Just As The Tide Was Flowing, Erin's Lovely Home* and *The Curry Rivel Wassail Song.*

Manuscript refs:
FT 226, 227, 233-239, 400-405, 2039-2043
FW 315-320, 327-331, 1911-1915
Photo refs: B26

STILL GROWING

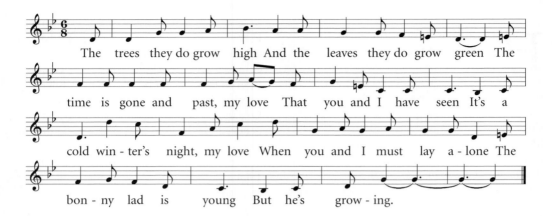

The trees they do grow high And the leaves they do grow green The
time is gone and past, my love That you and I have seen It's a
cold win-ter's night, my love When you and I must lay a-lone The
bon-ny lad is young But he's grow-ing.

The trees they do grow high
And the leaves they do grow green
The time is gone and past, my love
That you and I have seen
It's a cold winter's night, my love
When you and I must lay alone
The bonny lad is young
But he's growing.

'O father, dear father
I've feared you've done me harm
You've married me to a boy
And I fear he is too young.'
'O daughter, dearest daughter
And if you stay at home and wait along o' me
A lady you shall be
While he's growing.

We'll send him to the College
For one year or two
And then perhaps in time, my love
A man he may grow
I will buy you a bunch of white ribbons
To tie about his bonny, bonny waist
To let the ladies know
That he's married.'

At the age of sixteen
O he was a married man
At the age of seventeen
She brought to him a son
At the age of eighteen, my love
O his grave was growing green
And so she put an end
To his growing.

I made my love a shroud
Of the Holland so fine
And every stitch she put in it
The tears came trickling down
O once I had a sweetheart
But now I have got never a one
So fare you well, my own true love
For ever.

He is dead and buried
And in the churchyard laid
The green grass is over him
So very very thick.
O once I had a sweetheart
But now I have got never a one
So fare you well, my own true love
For ever.

Sharp made particular note of the singer's phrasing in subsequent verses, as follows:

Verse 2

O daughter, dear-est daugh - ter And if you stay at home and wait a-

long o' me A la - dy you shall be While he's grow-ing.

Verse 3

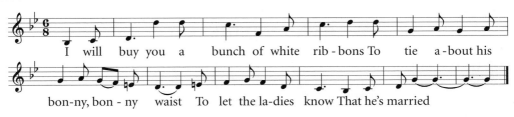

I will buy you a bunch of white rib - bons To tie a-bout his

bon-ny, bon - ny waist To let the la-dies know That he's married

Verse 4

At the age of eight-een, my love O his grave was grow-ing

green And so she put to an end to his grow-ing.

Verse 5

O once I had a sweet - heart But now I have got

ne-ver a one So fare you well, my own true love For e - ver.

MRS R. SAGE
Chew Stoke, Somerset

It has not been possible to identify **Mrs. R. Sage** of Chew Stoke, who provided the words and air for *Death and the Lady* in *Folk Songs from Somerset (Series Four)*. Sharp gives us information about the song, but not about the singer. It is not even clear whether R. is her initial or, as was usual at the time, her husband's.

We do know that Sharp visited her at least four times during 1907 and collected eight songs from her.

Manuscript refs:
FT 1161, 1170-1173, 1278, 1279, 2020
FW 1156-1158, 1162-1165, 1208-1210, 1888-1890
Photo refs: none

DEATH AND THE LADY

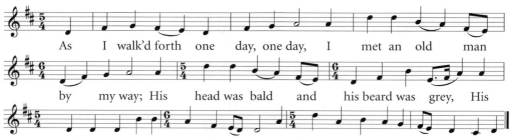

As I walk'd forth one day, one day, I met an old man by my way; His head was bald and his beard was grey, His clothing made of the cold earth of clay, His clothing made of the cold earth of clay.

As I walked forth one day, one day,
I met an old man by my way;
His head was bald and his beard was grey,
His clothing made of the cold earth of clay,
His clothing made of the cold earth of clay.

I say 'What man, what old man are you
Or what country do you belong unto?'
'My name is Death, han't you heard of me.
Both kings and princes bow down to me,
And you, fair maid, must come along with me.'

'I will give you gold, I will give you pearl,
I will give you costly rich robes to wear
If you will spare me a little while
A little long time my life for to amend.
A little long time my life for to amend.'

'I'll have none of your gold nor none of your
    pearl
Neither your costly rich robes to wear,
If you will spare me but a little while
A little longer time my life to amend.
A little longer time my life to amend.'

In six months after this fair maid died.
Let this be put on my tombstone, she cried.
Here lies a poor and distressed maid
Just in her bloom as she was snatched away
And her clothing was made of the cold earth clay.

JOHN SHORT
Watchet, Somerset

John Short of Watchet was Cecil Sharp's most prolific shanty singer. Between 20 April and 23 September 1914, he provided Sharp with 57 songs, mainly shanties, and was the main contributor to *English Folk-Chanteys*, providing 43 of the sixty songs published. Sharp described John's voice as:

… rich, resonant and powerful, and yet so flexible that he can execute trills, turns and graces with a delicacy and finish that would excite the envy of many a professed vocalist.

In her biography of Sharp, Maud Karpeles gave the following description of Short and Sharp together:

John Short liked to be near the sea when singing and so he and Cecil Sharp would sit side by side on the quay and John Short would sing happily through the noise of wind and waves while Cecil Sharp smoked his pipe and jotted down the tunes.

John Short was born in Watchet in March 1839 and in the 1850s went to sea on the brig *Promise*, bound for Cadiz and then Quebec. It was on this trip that he heard his first shanty, *Cheerily Man*. For the next fifty years John worked as a sailor, first on the deep-water ships sailing all over the world and then in the coastal trade. It was his time in the American ship, *Levant*, under a British flag of convenience that earned him the nickname, 'Yankee Jack'. Having a strong dislike of steamships, all but one of his many voyages at sea were in sailing ships.

Eventually John came ashore, owing to the ill health of his wife Annie, when he worked as a 'hobbler', a Bristol Channel name for a man who helped work ships in and out of harbour. His final working days were spent as town crier of Watchet and it is claimed that, with a following wind, he could be heard two miles away. John's son, George, commented that 'Cecil Sharp did a lot for father's voice'.

John's last public performance was at Watchet's manorial court leat in 1930, when he sang one of his favourite songs, *The Sweet Nightingale*: ''Tis not a sea song, but I often used to sing it aboard ship.'

John Short died on 9 April 1933, aged 94, and is one of the few able-bodied seamen to warrant an obituary in *The Times*, which appeared in the edition of 12 April 1933. Dr. A. A. Bockington wrote:

He always spoke with affection of Cecil Sharp, to whom he owed his reputation as a singer, though he himself thought little of reputation and much of homely things.

Manuscript refs:
FT 2877-2884, 2888-2894, 2896-2907, 2922-2929, 2935, 2936, 2944-2948, 2951, 2952, 2956-2962, 2998, 2999, 3059
FW none
Photo refs: A76-86

PADDY WORKS ON THE RAILWAY

In eighteen hundred and forty one
My corduroy breeches I put on
With a stick in my fist about two feet long
To work upon the railway, the railway
For I'm weary of the railway
O poor Paddy works on the railway.

In eighteen hundred and forty two
I thought this work would never do
And I resolved to put her through
A-working on the railway, the railway
etc.

In eighteen hundred and forty three
I paid my carriage across the sea
And in New York and Amerikee
To work upon the railway, the railway
etc.

In eighteen hundred and forty four
I landed on the Amerikee shore
And I resolved to work no more
To work upon the railway, the railway
etc.

I had a sister her name was Grace
Bad luck to her ugly face
She brought me to a deep disgrace
By working on the railway, the railway
etc.

JOANNE SLADE
Minehead, Somerset

During visits on 8 August 1904 and 15 January 1906, **Mrs Joanne Slade** of Minehead sang three songs for Sharp, one of which, *Hares on the Mountain*, was mentioned in *Folk Songs from Somerset (Series One)*. At the time of the 1901 census, Mrs Slade (54) was living in Quay Street with her sailor husband William (54), and four sons, Henry (21), Frederick (13), Ernest (11) and William (8). There were two lodgers, George Andrews and another William Slade, living with them.

Manuscript refs:
FT 272, 274, 772
FW 378-380
Photo refs: none

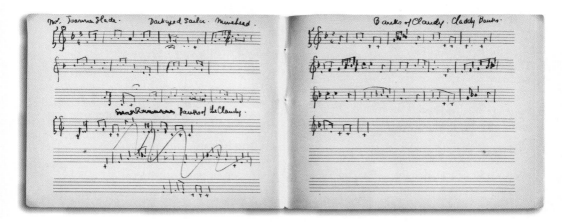

From Sharp's field notebook

BANKS OF CLAUDY

As I walked out one morning
All in the month of May
Down through some flowery gardens
I carelessly did stray.
I overheard a damsel
In sorrow to complain
Now for her absent lover
That ploughs the raging main.

I stepped up to this fair maid,
I put her in surprise
I own she did not know me,
I being dressed in disguise.
Says I: 'My lovely maiden,
My joy and heart's delight,
How far have you to wander
This dark and dreary night.'

'All the way, kind sir, to Cloddy,
If you will please to show
Pity a poor girl distracted,
It's there I have to go.
I'm in search of a faithless young man
And Johnny is his name,
And on the banks of Cloddy
I'm told he does remain.

If my Johnny he was here this night
He'd keep me from all harm,
But he's in the field of battle
All in his uniform.
He's in the field of battle,
His foes he will destroy,
Like a roving king of honour
He fought on the banks of Troy.'

'O 'tis six months and better
Since your Johnny left the shore,
He's a-cruising the wide ocean
Where foaming billows roar,
He's a-cruising the wide ocean
For honour and for gain.
The ship's been wrecked as I am told
All on the coast of Spain.'

As soon as she heard him say so
She fell into deep despair
By wringing of her milk-white hands.
And tearing of her hair.
'If my Johnny he be drownded
No man on earth I'll take
But through lonesome groves and valleys
I will wander for his sake.'

As soon as he heard her say so
He could no longer stand
But he fell into her arms
Saying: 'Bessie, I'm the man,
I am that faithless young man
Whom you thought was slain
And once we've met on Cloddy banks
We'll never part again.'

ELIZABETH SMITHERD
Tewkesbury, Gloucestershire

Elizabeth Smitherd was born in 1845 in the small village of Pamington in Gloucestershire. She told Sharp that her father, John Haines, a carpenter, was 'a squire's son'. She was one of thirteen sisters and learned all her songs from them, as well as from her father and her mother, Ann. She married a Chelsea Pensioner from Derby, Joseph Smitherd, and the couple set up home at 5 Station Road in the nearby town of Tewkesbury. Sharp met Mrs Smitherd whilst staying in Tewkesbury for a couple of days, during January 1908, probably at the guest house in Abbey Terrace run by the Misses Moody and Brace, and revisited her in April the same year, noting a total of 19 songs, including fine versions of *Our Captain Cried All Hands* and *The Miser*.

Elizabeth Smitherd died in 1910.

Paul Burgess

Manuscript refs:
FT 1571-1577, 1626-1631, 1640-1645
FW 1417-1421, 1479-1487, 1492-1499
Photo refs: none

POACHING SONG

When I was bound apprentice In famous Somersetshire I serv'd my master truly For nearly seven year, Till I took up to poaching As you shall quickly hear For 'twas my delight of a shiny night In the season of the year.

When I was bound apprentice
In famous Somersetshire
I served my master truly
For nearly seven year,
Till I took up to poaching
As you shall quickly hear
For 'twas my delight of a shiny night
In the season of the year.

As me and my companions
Were setting of a snare
The gamekeeper was watching us
But for him we did not care
For we can wrestle fight, my boys,
Jump over anywhere.
For it's my delight, etc.

As me and my companions
Were setting for a five
In taking of them up again

We caught a hare alive
We popped her in the bag, my boys,
And through the woods did steer
For it's my delight, etc.

We threw her across our shoulders
And wandered through the town,
And called into a neighbour's house
And sold her for a crown,
We sold her for a crown, my boys,
But dare not tell you where,
For it's my delight, etc.

So here's success to poachers
For I do not think it fair,
Bad luck to every gamekeeper
That will not sell his deer.
Good luck to every landlady
That wants to buy a hare.
For it's my delight, etc.

TOM SPRACKLAN
Hambridge, Somerset

Tom Spracklan, who supplied Sharp with twelve songs during at least three visits between September 1903 and January 1904, had been a soldier prior to working for George Duncan Templeman as cowman at Earnshill Farm, Hambridge, one of the largest farms in the area. Templeman was a great advocate for the song collecting activities of Sharp and Marson and provided three songs himself.

Sharp described Tom as having a very innocent face and would sing with a transfixed expression pointed to the ceiling. He was also known to have a more sinister side and had become agitated when singing *Brennan on the Moor*. In a lecture note of November 1903, Sharp claimed that he had bitten a man's thumb off a few weeks earlier!

In the 1901 census, Tom appears as Theodore Spracklan, 'Cowman on Farm', aged 42, 'born in Dorset, exact location not known'. His wife Alice was 39 and born at Upottery, Devon. Of their five children, Albert (14), Annie (12), Walter (5) and William (7) had all been born in Dorset, whilst the youngest, Hilda (3), was born in Hambridge.

Manuscript refs:
FT 18, 22, 23, 28-30, 33, 37, 41, 104-106
FW 29, 30, 37-40, 47-54, 61, 62, 67, 68, 73, 74, 99, 101, 102
Photo refs: none

Spracklan's version of High Germany as it appeared in Journal of the Irish Folk Song Society, London, vol 1, no 1, April 1904

George Templeman

BONNY BUNCH OF ROSES

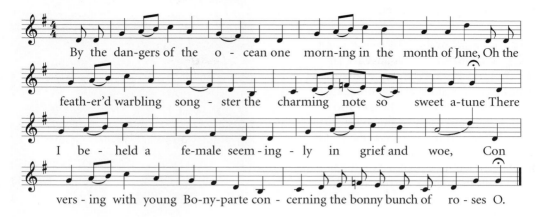

By the dan-gers of the o - cean one morn-ing in the month of June, Oh the feath-er'd warbling song - ster the charming note so sweet a-tune There I be - held a fe-male seem-ing - ly in grief and woe, Con vers - ing with young Bo-ny-parte con - cerning the bonny bunch of ro - ses O.

By the dangers of the ocean, one morning in the month of June,
Oh the feathered warbling songster the charming note so sweet a-tune,
There I beheld a female seemingly in grief and woe,
Conversing with young Bonyparte concerning the bonny bunch of roses O.

'Oh then,' said young Napoleon and grabst [grabbed] his mother by the hand:
'O mother do have patience until I'm able to command.
I will raise a mighty army and through tremjus [tremendous] dangers go,
And in spite of all the universe I'll gain you the bonny bunch of roses O.'

['Oh son, don't be so venturesome, for England has he hearts of oak,
There's England, Ireland and Scotland, their unity has never been broke.
Oh son, look at your father, in St. Helena his body lies low,
And you will follow after, so beware of the bonny bunch of roses O.']

When you saw great Bonyparte you fell down on your bended knees,
And asked your father's life of him and he granted it right manfully,
['Twas then he took an army and over foreign realms did go,
He said he'd conquer Moscow, then go to the bonny bunch of roses O].

It was there he took an army and likewise kings to join his throne,
He was so well provided, enough to sweep the world all through.
But when he came near Moscow, near overpowered by driving snow,
Moscow was a-blazing there he lost all the bonny bunch of roses O.

'Adieu, adieu for ever and now I'm on my dying bed
If I had lived I should have been clever, now droop my youthful head.
For while our bones doth moulder and weeping willows over us grow
By the deeds of bold Napoleon, concerning the bonny bunch of roses O.'

WILLIAM STOKES
Chew Stoke, Somerset

According to the 1901 census return, **William Stokes** was an 'Ordinary Agricultural Labourer', aged 58, and widowed, living alone at The Street, Chew Stoke. In his earlier career he had also worked as a miner. According to local tradition, he was the sidesman, the sexton, the pew-opener, and a stonemason, which may mean that he specialised in building the stone walls that define the fields on the Mendip Hills. He was remembered for his great silver watch chain.

Bill Stokes was a prolific singer who provided Sharp with thirty-three songs, two of which were published in *Folk Songs from Somerset*. Collecting the songs entailed at least eight visits between 1906 and 1909.

Sharp noted that *Irish Molly O* had come from an 'old Ballet seller from Bath', although Bill knew it before, and that *The Sailor and the Soldier* came from Moses Yates of Winford, Bill's native village, 'who would now be 130 yrs old if alive'.

William Stokes died in December 1915, aged 73.

Manuscript refs:
FT 1070-1076, 1087-1094, 1159, 1160, 1174-1176, 1277, 1520-1524, 2021, 2163-2168
FW 1077-1081, 1090-1093, 1155, 1166, 1167, 1207, 1357-1361, 1891, 1892, 2025-2032
Photo refs: A7

The Sailor and the Soldier – from Sharp's field notebook

THE SAILOR AND THE SOLDIER

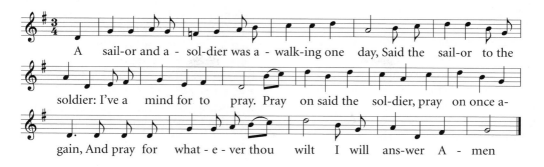

A sailor and a soldier was a-walking one day, Said the sailor to the soldier: I've a mind for to pray. Pray on said the soldier, pray on once again, And pray for whatever thou wilt I will answer A - men

A sailor and a soldier was a-walking one day,
Said the sailor to the soldier: 'I've a mind for to pray.'
'Pray on,' said the soldier, 'pray on once again,
And pray for whatever thou wilt I will answer Amen.'

'The first thing they came to was an old hollow tree.'
Said the sailor to the soldier: 'This my pulpit shall be.'
'Pray on,' said the soldier, 'pray on once again,
And pray for whatever thou wilt I will answer Amen.'

'The first thing I'll pray for, I'll pray for our King,
That he have peace and plenty all the days of his reign,
And where he got one man I wish he had ten,
And never never want an army.' Said the soldier: 'Amen.'

'The next thing I'll pray for I'll pray for the King,
That he have peace and plenty all the days of his reign,
And where he got one ship I wish he had ten,
And never never want for navy.' Said the soldier: 'Amen.'

'The next thing I'll pray for is a pot of good beer,
For good liquors were sent our spirits to cheer,
And where we got one pot I wish we had ten,
And never never want for liquor.' Said the soldier: 'Amen.'

ELIZA SWEET
Somerton, Somerset

On the night of the 1901 census, the Sweet household at Somerton numbered eleven: Alfred Sweet, a 54 year old shoemaker working at home; his wife **Eliza Sweet**, also 54 and, like her husband, born at Merriott; seven children, who were Bessie (24), Rose (19), George (17), Elsie (16), Walter (14), Eleaner (11) and Ethel (9); a 2 year old boarder, Albert Owen; and a 2 month old grandson, Victor H. Sweet. The children and the grandson were all born in Somerton, but Albert Owen was born in Hendon, London.

Sharp collected five songs from Mrs Sweet and a further song, *Jan's Courtship*, was sent to him by Miss Alice Snow, a musical schoolmistress whose father, mother and grandmother also sang for Sharp. Interestingly, Sharp noted *Searching for Lambs* twice in those five songs, and published it in *Folk Songs from Somerset (Series Four)* where he describes it as 'the most perfect song of its type that I have recovered in Somerset'.

Manuscript refs:
FT 959, 960, 1099, 1409-1411
FW 1001-1003, 1086, 1087, 1295, 1296,
Photo refs: none

QUEEN JANE

Queen Jane was in labour
For six days or more
Till the women got tired
And wished it all o'er.

'Good women, good women,
Good women if you be,
Will you send for King Henry,
King Henry I must see.'

King Henry was a-sent for,
King Henry did come home
For to meet with Queen Jane, my love,
Your eyes look so dim.

'King Henry, King Henry,
King Henry if you be,
Will you have my right side cut open
You will find my dear baby.'

'Queen Jane, my love, Queen Jane, my love.
Such things were never known;
If you open your right side
You will lose your dear baby.'

'Will you build your love a castle
And lie down so deep
For to bury my body
And to christen my dear baby.'

King Henry went mourning
And so did his men
And so did his dear baby
For Queen Jane did die then.

And how deep was the mourning,
How wide was the bands,
How yellow was the flower, my boys,
She carried in her hands.

How she hold it, how she rumpled it,
How she hold it in her hand,
Saying: 'The flower of old England
Shall never detain me long.'

There was fiddling, there was dancing
The day the babe was born;
To see that Queen Jane, my love,
Lying cold as a stone.

JOHN THORNE
Minehead, Somerset

John Thorne lived in Minehead and was visited by Sharp in January 1906 when he provided the collector with two songs, both of which were used in the Minehead mummers' play. Described as John Thorne of Alcombe, Minehead, 'a Minehead Mummer of long ago', he also provided the text of the play for Clement Kille, a local journalist, editor, author and collector of folklore. In January 1909, the mummers' play was revived and performed by members of the Guild of St George, a Minehead association whose president was the Rev. F. M. Etherington. Etherington collaborated with and entertained Sharp during the many visits the collector made to the area.

At the time of the 1901 census, John Thorne was living with his unmarried daughter and granddaughter. His trade is given as 'Stone Mason'.

Manuscript refs:
FT 768, 769
FW 827-829
Photo refs: none

MUMMERS' SONG

Of music merrily play
And of cannons loudly roar.
You're welcome home St George
Home to your native shore.

O the next we do call in
It is our noble king
Who is lately come from the wars
Glad tidings he doth bring.

Although I've been in the wars
It's not for any harm,
It's all for the sake of my love
Because I was so young.

Although I have been tried
In cities towns and fields
But never could get that man
That ever could make me yield.

Hodge Podge I have forgot
It's one all of our crew
And if I must tell you please
My dear I'm in love with you.

Of music change your tune
And play up merrily
That we may have a dance
For to please our company.

CAPTAIN JAMES VICKERY
Minehead, Somerset

During five visits between 1904 and 1907, **Captain James Vickery** supplied Sharp with ten songs, mostly sea songs, two of which appeared in *Folk Songs from Somerset*. Little is known of Captain Vickery, apart from what is found in the census returns. In 1881 he was a 42 year old mariner who lived with his wife, Eliza, five years his senior, in Quay Street, Minehead, both having been born in Carhampton. A granddaughter, Alice Sparkes, lived with them. Twenty years later, Alice was still living with them in Quay Street, but Eliza's occupation had changed from seamstress to midwife.

Manuscript refs:
FT 273, 275, 279, 280, 570, 571, 773, 774, 1432, 1433
FW 381, 382, 646, 647, 830, 1315-1318
Photo refs: B45

PRINCESS ROYAL

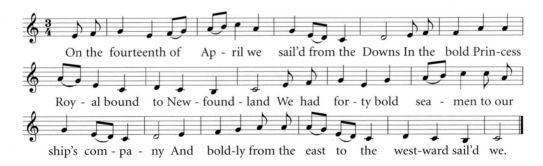

On the fourteenth of April we sail'd from the Downs In the bold Princess Roy-al bound to New-found-land We had for-ty bold sea-men to our ship's com-pa-ny And bold-ly from the east to the west-ward sail'd we.

On the fourteenth of April we sailed from the Downs
In the bold *Princess Royal* bound to Newfoundland
We had forty bold seamen to our ship's company
And boldly from the east to the westward sailed we.

We had not been sailing many days but two or three
When a man at our masthead a sail he did spy
Come bearing down on us to see what we were
While under her mizzen peak black colours she wore.

'Good lord!' said our captain, 'what shall we do now?
Here comes a bold pirate to rob us, I know.'
'Oh no!' cried our chief mate, 'that never can be so,
For we'll shake out our reefs, boys, and from her we'll go.'

So then this bold pirate he came alongside,
With a loud speaking trumpet 'Whence came you?' he cried,
Our captain being aloft he answered him so,
'We come from fair London, bound to Kallio.'

'Then haul up your courses and heel your ship to,
For I have some letters I'll send home by you.'
'Yes I'll haul up my courses and heave my ship to,
It shall be in some harbour, not alongside o' you.'

Then hoist up your topsails, top gallants also,
Your stay sails and royals and from her we'll go.
He fired some shots after us, but of no avail,
For the bold *Princess Royal* she showed him her tail.

Then he chased us to windward, he chased us all day,
He chased us to windward until the next day,
Then he hauled up his courses and from us bore away

'Thank God,' cried our captain, 'since the pirate is gone,
Go down to your grog, boys, go down every one,
Go down to your grog, boys, and be of good cheer,
For as long as we've sail room, my lads never fear.'

Bridgwater Quay

LUCY WHITE
Hambridge, Somerset

Lucy White of Westport, Hambridge, was the sister (possibly the half-sister) of Louie Hooper and, together, the source of one hundred songs noted by Cecil Sharp. In 1901, Lucy was 53 and married to John White, an agricultural engine driver. Five unmarried children were living with them: agricultural labourers John (27) and Nathaniel (17), along with Bessie (19), Polly (15) and Maud (13), all shirt and button-hole makers. Lucy and John had at least two other daughters living elsewhere.

In *Folk Songs from Somerset (First Series)*, the Rev. Charles Marson relates how the sisters became acquainted with Sharp:

Then we applied to two sisters, Mrs. Hooper and Mrs. White, and to the dairyman at Earnshill Barn, Mr. Tom Sprachlan. These three most kindly came up to the Parsonage, and surprised us by the wealth and variety of the songs they knew.

In the *Musical Herald* of 1 December 1905, Sharp wrote of Lucy White and Louie Hooper:

They really are fine singers. They never mix their tunes; they are always clear; they sing with perfect intonation; they are ready at a moment's notice to sing any song; yet they are unable to read or write … The elder of the two (Lucy White) is only fifty eight. They told me that they learned nearly all their songs from their mother, who died three or four years ago. I have traced many of the best songs of the district to her. Singers often told me, when I have mentioned a song, 'Ah, that is one of Mrs. England's songs'. She must have been a great singer.

There is evidence that Louie and Lucy's great-grandmother, a Bussell from Buckland St Mary, was known as a singer for some distance around. With this background it is not surprising that Lucy sang from a very young age. As a child she sang the songs along the country lanes of a summer's evening, but eventually had to restrict herself

to singing them at home due to complaints from the 'Methodies'!

Sharp also noted where some of the other songs were learnt. *The False Bride*, which Sharp reckoned to be the finest song he collected, with one exception, was learnt on the beach at Weston-super-Mare; *Seventeen Come Sunday* from her aunt, Hannah Bond, of Barrington, who died the following Sunday; and *The Golden Glove* from her cousin, John Vicary, who worked on Lord Digby's estate at Sherborne, Dorset.

Lucy White died in 1923, aged 74, after a prolonged illness which kept her bed-ridden for the last four years of her life.

Manuscript refs:
FT 75, 76, 166, 167, 189, 190, 194, 195, 197, 220-222, 267-271, 317, 318, 321. 323, 384, 504-508, 510, 511, 518-520, 601, 602, 646, 690, 850, 851
FW 106, 112, 254, 255, 287, 290, 291, 293, 294, 308, 310, 375-377, 430, 431, 444, 447, 512, 590, 591, 692, 715, 765
Photo refs: B10

With Louie Hooper:
Manuscript refs:
FT 3, 6-12, 14-16, 19-21, 24-27, 34, 38, 39, 50-54, 63-66, 77-79
FW 3-5, 11-22, 25-27, 31-35, 41-46, 63, 64, 69-71, 81, 82, 85-90, 92, 93, 105, 286

COME BUY MY FINE HERRINGS

Come buy my fine her-rings, My fine sil-ver her-rings, Come buy my fine her-rings, That's just return'd from sea. Come buy, come buy, you are too late, Mark how they're sel-ling While the merry merry bells shall ring.

Come buy my fine herrings,
My fine silver herrings,
Come buy my fine herrings,
That's just returned from sea.
Come buy, come buy, you are too late,
Mark how they are selling
While the merry merry bells shall ring.

We cast a net so long at sea (3 times)
And a very fine catch had we.

We cast our net all on the deep (3 times)
And the devil of a fish catched we.

FAREWELL HE

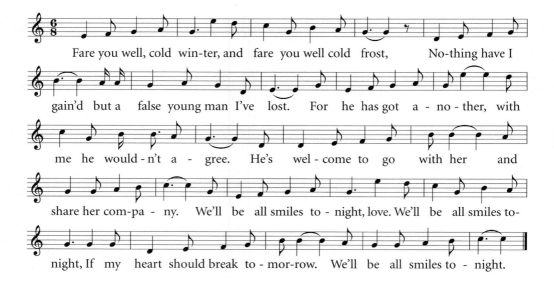

Fare you well, cold win-ter, and fare you well cold frost, No-thing have I gain'd but a false young man I've lost. For he has got a-no-ther, with me he would-n't a-gree. He's wel-come to go with her and share her com-pa-ny. We'll be all smiles to-night, love. We'll be all smiles to-night, If my heart should break to-mor-row. We'll be all smiles to-night.

Fare you well, cold winter, and fare you well cold frost,
Nothing have I gained but a false young man I've lost.
For he has got another, with me he wouldn't agree.
He's welcome to go with her and share her company.

Chorus
   We'll be all smiles to-night, love.
   We'll be all smiles to-night,
   If my heart should break tomorrow.
   We'll be all smiles to-night.

The last time I did meet him 'twas down a shady grove
He looked at me and smiled and handed me a rose.
Do you think that I would take it? O no, my love, not I.
Before I'd humble to my love I'd lay me down and die.

He wrote to me a letter to tell me he was sad.
I wrote one back to him again and told him I was glad.
I told him to keep his paper and I would keep my time,
For I care no more for his false heart than he do care for mine.

NO MY LOVE NOT I or NEWFOUNDLAND SAILOR

O the ve-ry best thing that I can 'vise you I can 'vise you for to
do Is to take the babe all on your back And a beg-ging for to
go. And when that you are tired You can set down and
cry, Yes and curse the ve-ry hour You said, No my love not
I. When fish-es fly and swal-lows die Then young men will prove
true There's a herb in your fa-ther's gar-den And some do call it rue.

O the very best thing that I can 'vise you
I can 'vise you for to do
Is to take the babe all on your back
And a begging for to go.
And when that you are tired
You can set down and cry,
Yes and curse the very hour
You said, No my love not I.

When fishes fly and swallows die
Then young men will prove true
There's a herb in your father's garden
And some do call it rue.

So go down in your father's garden
And sit and cry your fill
And when you think on what you've done
You blame your own free will.

Since the lands they are so long
And you thought yourself so high
Do you think that ever I will marry you?
O no my love not I.

As I walked out one morning, all in the month of May,
There I spied a fair pretty maid a-gathering of sweet hay,
I asked her if she'd wed with me, I'd marry her by 'n' by,
But the answer that she gave to me: 'Not I, my love, not I.'

Two or three months came after this and then
This pretty fair damsel growed thicker round her waist,
Her gown it would not pin, my boys, her apron strings won't tie,
And she cursed the very hour when she said: 'No, my love, not I.'

She wrote a letter unto him to come immediately,
But the answer he returned again: 'Not I, my love, not I.
Supposing I should come to you, shouldn't I be much to blame?
My parents would be angry, they'd laugh at my disdain.'

[If I, love, should marry you my parents they would frown,
My friends and relations they would me disown]
I think that you're so very low and I'm so very high,
Do you think that I could marry you? 'Not I, my love, not I.'

The best thing that I can advise you for to do
Is to take your baby to your back and a-begging for to go,
And when that you are weary, love, you may sit down and cry,
And curse the very hour that you said: 'No, my love, not I.'
And when that you are weary, love, you may sit down and cry,
And curse the very hour that you said: 'No, my love, not I.'

Mary Overd, Lucy White, Sarah Hutchings, Louisa Hooper, Liza Hutchings

SUSAN WILLIAMS
Haselbury Plucknett, Somerset

In the *Musical Times* of 1 January 1907, Cecil Sharp wrote the following about **Susan Williams** of Haselbury Plucknett:

Old singers, wonderful as are their memories, have yet forgotten many of the songs they used to know. As an old singer once said, speaking about me, to a mutual friend 'Ah! If that young man had a come to me forty years ago I'd a zung 'un out o' zight'. That was old Susan Williams of Haselbury Plucknett, one of the most delightful singers and pleasant companions it has been my good fortune to meet. Susan is a widow, seventy five years old, and she lives alone in as pretty a cottage as you could wish to see. I cannot reproduce the charm of her voice – sweet and pure as the note of the woodland thrush – but her winsome face and picturesque appearance I can show by means of the accompanying photograph.

I have taken down nearly fifty songs from her lips. 'Farewell Nancy' is perhaps the finest tune I have gained from her, but she has given me plenty of good ones besides.

There are 22 songs from Susan Williams in the Sharp manuscripts, an indication that he considered almost half of her repertoire worth noting. As elsewhere, Sharp appears to have been seeking old songs from old singers, not their current repertoire. Four of her songs appear in *Folk Songs from Somerset*, including *The Keys of Heaven*, of which she remembered just one verse and the tune from a single hearing some 30 or 40 years earlier when the mummers had performed it. She learnt the version of *Lord Bateman* from her father. About *Searching for Lambs* she made the following comment: 'I learnt this when I warn't 10 year old.'

In 1908, Sharp was presented with a watercolour painting of Susan Williams, which further endorses the mutual respect and affection that existed between him and his singers.

Susan's husband, John, died in 1886 at the age of 55. A son, Bob, died at only 28 in 1899, and Susan herself passed away on 4 March 1915, aged 83. The 1901 census provides little additional information to Sharp's description of her, except that she was a web weaver working at home.

Manuscript refs:
FT 593-595, 625-631, 698-700, 703-708, 854, 855, 1779
FW 672-674, 702-707, 782-786, 791-796, 923-926, 1615, 1616
Photo refs: B50

THE BLUE COCKADE

'Twas on one Whitsun morning
As I rode over the moss,
I had no thought of 'listing
Till a soldier did me cross.
Bad company enticed me
To drink the ale so brown,
Whilst advancing, still advancing
With some money ten guineas and a crown.

'Tis my true love has 'listed
He wears a blue cockade
He's a handsome tall young man
Likewise a roving blade.
He's a handsome tall young man.
He's gone to serve the Queen
Whilst my very, still my very
Heart is breaking all for the loss of him.

O may he never prosper,
O may he never thrive,
Nor anything he takes in hand
So long as he's alive.
May the very ground that he treads on,
May the grass refuse to grow,
Since he's been, still he's been
My only sorrow, grief and woe.

I'll go down in some valley
And mourning for my true love.
I'll write his name on every tree
That stands on yonder grove.
The huntsman they shall holloa
And the hounds shall make a noise
For to find, still to find
In my true lover's arms ten thousand charms of joy.

SUSAN WILSON
Shipham, Somerset

Susan Wilson of Shipham, Somerset, sang three songs for Sharp on 24 April 1906. None of them was published in *Folk Songs from Somerset*. At the time of the 1901 census, Susan was a 66 year old shop keeper 'in Grocers', widowed and living with three bachelor sons, Christopher (39), William (34) and James (31). All three sons were agricultural labourers.

Manuscript refs:
FT 935-937
FW 994, 995
Photo refs: none

LONG TAILED BLUE

I've just come in to see you all To ask how do you do. I'll sing you a song and it's not ve-ry long It's a - bout my long-tailed blue. How do you like my blue? Look at my long-tail'd Blue. I'll sing you a song and it's not ve - ry long It's a - bout my long tail'd blue

I've just come in to see you all
To ask how do you do.
I'll sing you a song and it's not very long
It's about my long-tailed blue.

How do you like my blue?
Look at my long-tailed Blue.
I'll sing you a song and it's not very long
It's about my long tailed blue

Some people have got but one coat
You see I have got two.
I wear a jacket all the week,
On Sundays I wear my blue.

As I was going up Market Street
A-holloa after Sue.
The watchman came and picked me up
And split my long-tailed blue.

I took him to a tailor's shop
To see what he could do.
He took a needle and some thread
And mended my long-tailed blue.

If you want to gain the lady's health
I'll tell you what to do.
You go to the tip top tailor's shop
And buy a long tailed blue.

JIM WOODLAND
Stocklinch, Somerset

Jim Woodland was a navy pensioner, shopkeeper and parish clerk at Stocklinch, Somerset. There was a strong tie with the Navy in the Woodland family, Jim and five brothers having served at the same time. It is therefore surprising that he was known as 'Soldier' Jim, but that probably had something to do with his upright posture and brisk walking pace.

Jim was related to at least two of the other singers who sang for Sharp: Lizzie Welch and Jane Ree, both of whom were Woodlands before marriage. He gave Sharp and Charles Marson a total of three songs in December 1903 and April 1904. The words that he provided for *Brimbledon Fair, or Young*

Rambleaway, were used to supplement a text recorded elsewhere.

By the 1901 census there are two James Woodlands in Stocklinch, one a farmer in Stocklinch Magdalen and the other an 'Ordinary Agricultural Labourer' in the adjoining Stocklinch Ottersay. As the cottage where he lived is known, the singer must have been the labourer, then aged 59, living with his wife Jane (49). They had a large family and there were still seven children living at home at the time of the census: Tom (16), Minnie (14), Annie (12), Daisy (10), Edith (8), Hilda (5) and Herbert (3).

Manuscript refs:
FT 57, 58, 159
FW 95, 96, 241, 242
Photo refs: none

BRIMBLEDOWN FAIR

As I was a-going to Brimbledown Fair
I saw pretty Nancy a-curdling her hair.
I gave her a wink and she rolled her dark eye,
At night to myself I'll be wi' you by and bye.

As you are going to Brimbledown Fair
You'll see some sweet lasses as you passes on,
You'll see some sweet lasses but, mind and take care
That you don't get brimbled at Brimbledown Fair.

So keep your time in order, young lasses and open in time
And take care when returning from Brimbledown Fair.

AS I WAS GOING TO DERRY DOWN FAIR

As I was a-going to Derrydown Fair
With my scarlet coat and everything there
'Twas in order to entice all buxom and gay
That wished for to go with young ramble away
Ramble away,
That wished for to go with young ramble away.

O the very first steps I put into the fair
I saw pretty Nancy a-combing her hair
I topped her the wink and she rolled her black eye
Thinks I to myself I'll be with you by and by, *etc.*

O as I was walking at night in the dark
I took pretty Nancy to be my sweetheart
She smiled in my face these words she did say
'Are you the young lad that's called Ramble away,' *etc.*

O I said, 'Pretty Nancy don't smile in my face
For I do not intend to stay long in this place.'
So I gave her three doubles and fair length and share
I told her I'd ramble but didn't know where, *etc.*

Now come all you pretty maids wherever you be
From this jolly banquet I'll have you go free
My hat, cap and feathers my dear you shall wear
And a bunch of blue ribbon to tie up your hair, *etc.*

GEORGE WYATT
West Harptree, Somerset

Cecil Sharp first visited **George Wyatt** in April 1904. Wyatt was 78 years old at the time. At their initial meeting Sharp noted only one song but returned during his stay at Harptree Court to note another. Of the two songs, one was *Blackbirds and Thrushes*. Subsequently, Sharp noted another six songs and visited Wyatt on five occasions in all. One of the songs, *Lord Randall*, had been sung by George's brother, Samuel, who was known locally as 'Spotted-on-the-back Sammy' from a line of the song. Sammy had died sometime before Sharp visited West Harptree.

George and his wife, Lydia, lived in a low, single storey 'key cottage' at Blue Bowl, West Harptree. A key cottage, also known as a squatter's cottage, is one that is built in a restricted time (usually dawn to dusk, or vice versa) on common land, and smoke has to be seen coming from the chimney at the end of the allotted time. Ownership is not by deed but by possession of the key to the door. The cottage was described as being of wattle and daub, with a single room divided by a wooden partition. The sleeping quarters are on the left in the photograph. According to the 1881 census, the Wyatt family included a daughter and three sons. George was an agricultural labourer, remembered for driving horses with a firkin of cider hung on the hames, while Lydia raised the family, looked after the home and kept chickens which were tethered by one leg to stop them getting into the garden.

George Wyatt died in December 1907, aged 85. Lydia lived on in the cottage on her own for many years after, receiving parish relief of 2/6 (12½p) and a loaf of bread. She is remembered for her bonnet, her gleaming white apron, a fire on a huge heap of ashes that never went out, her strong black tea and her reputation as a witch, although she was really a friendly old soul who loved to 'bide and chat'. She died in 1916 in Clutton Poor Law Infirmary, aged 88.

Manuscript refs:
FT 198, 205, 206, 358, 362, 363, 512, 514, 515
FW 278, 279, 483, 484, 486
Photo refs: B12

BLACKBIRDS AND THRUSHES

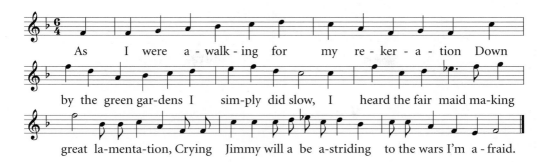

As I were a-walking for my rekeration [recreation]
Down by the green gardens I simply did slow,
I heard the fair maid making great lamentation,
Crying: Jimmy will a be a-striding to the wars I'm afraid.

The blackbirds and thrushes down by the green bushes
They all seem to mourn for this fair maid,
Crying the song that she sung was concerning her lover
Jimmy will be a-sliding to the wars I'm afraid.

And Jimmy will return with his heart full of burning
To see his love Nancy lie dead in her grave
Young man forsaken he died in a week
Crying so he had never have left this fair maid.

Success may attend every lad on the ocean
God send him safe home to his sweetheart and wives
For peace may be claiming in every nation
God send my soldier safe home to his bride.

WORKHOUSES (UNIONS)

A sweep through Cecil Sharp's manuscripts somewhat undermines the rustic image of man on bicycle embarking on a great quest through the leafy lanes of England's most rural beauty spots. What it actually shows is that towns and even cities were certainly on his agenda as sources for music and songs, and in fact he spent concentrated and very productive periods working within them. This is borne out by his use of workhouses as fertile grounds for his collecting. For Sharp collected or received almost 250 tunes from their transient residents between 1905 and 1923, and from as far afield as Northumberland, Herefordshire, Shropshire, Wiltshire, Somerset, Essex and Cambridgeshire. However, it was the Marylebone Workhouse in London which was by far the most important, and here, between September 1908 and September 1914, he amassed 98 tunes from 26 inhabitants, paying 20 separate visits during October 1908 alone.

W. SMITH

W. Smith or John Murphy?

Within its walls he found **W. Smith**, aged 63, who could be the subject of our photograph here, although it is more likely to be John Murphy, from whom he noted down 29 songs during sixteen visits in 1908 and 1909. W. Smith gave Sharp only the one song on his very first visit. As you might expect, the 1901 census throws up a whole host of Smiths and two by the name of William. As neither would have been 63 in 1908, it seems that our singer was not resident.

Manuscript refs:
FT 1934
FW none
Photo refs: none confirmed

THE LAKE OF COUL FIN

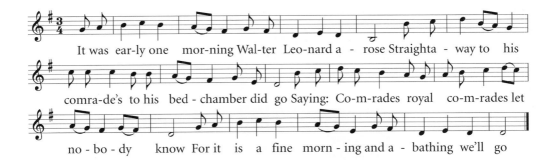

It was ear-ly one mor-ning Wal-ter Leo-nard a-rose Straighta-way to his comra-de's to his bed-chamber did go Saying: Co-m-rades royal co-m-rades let no-bo-dy know For it is a fine morn-ing and a-bathing we'll go

It was early one morning Walter Leonard arose
Straightaway to his comrade's bed-chamber did go
Saying: 'Comrades royal comrades let nobody know
For it is a fine morning and a-bathing we'll go.'

THE LAKES OF COALFLIN

It was early one morning young William arose,
Straight away to his comrade's bedchamber did go,
Saying, 'Comrade, dear comrade, don't let anyone know,
For it is a fine morning, and a-bathing we'll go.'

As they went along it was down a long lane,
But who should they meet but a keeper of game,
Saying, 'I would advise you to return home again,
For there's death in false waters in the lakes of Coalflin.'

Young William stepped in and he swam the lakes round,
He swam to the island but not the right ground,
Saying, 'Comrade, dear comrade, do not adventure in,
For your doom is to die in a watery stream.'

It was early the next morning his mother she was there,
She rode round the island [like one in despair]
Saying, 'Where was he drownded or did he fall in?
For there's death in false waters in the lakes of Coalflin.'

God help his poor mother; she has reasons to mourn,
Likewise his dear sweetheart; she has reasons to mourn,
For every each other morning he did her salute
With the pinks and red roses and the fine garden fruit.

At the day of his funeral it will be a good sight,
There'll be four and twenty Irish girls and they'll all dress in white,
They'll carry him along and lay him in cold clay,
Saying adieu to young William, and they'll all march away.

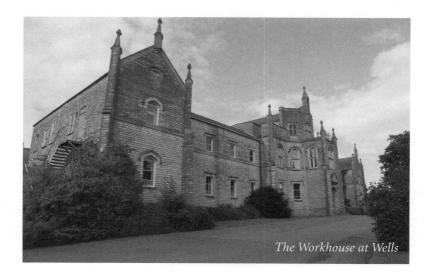

The Workhouse at Wells

THOMAS GREEN

In August 1908, Sharp visited William Walter and **Thomas Green** in Wells Union, Somerset. While he took down two songs from William, it is the sole rendition from Thomas that is reproduced here. Sharp noted that he was 62 years of age at the time. The 1901 census tells us that he was one of 141 residents, a 56 year old unmarried pauper, whose employment was given as 'Bootm (sic) Formerly Shoemaker'.

Manuscript refs:
FT 1803
FW none
Photo refs: none

DILLY SONG

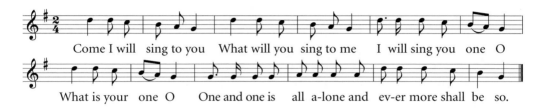

Come I will sing to you What will you sing to me I will sing you one O

What is your one O One and one is all a-lone and ev-er more shall be so.

Come I will sing to you
What will you sing to me
I will sing you one O
What is your one O
One and one is all alone
  and ever more shall be so.

Two of them was lily white babes
  and they were clothed in green O
Three of them were drivers
Four the gospel preachers
Five the ploughboys under the bush
Six the nimble waiters
Seven the seven stars under the sky
Eight the Gabriel angels
Nine and nine the bright come shine
Ten is the commandments
Eleven and eleven is going to heaven
And twelve's the twelve apostles.

In the last verse these phrases are distributed thus:

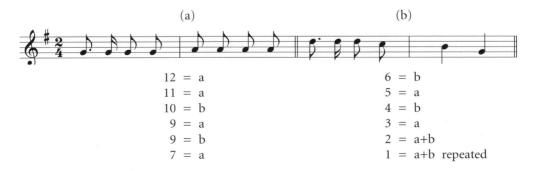

(a)	(b)
12 = a	6 = b
11 = a	5 = a
10 = b	4 = b
9 = a	3 = a
9 = b	2 = a+b
7 = a	1 = a+b repeated

MRS TRUBY

Mrs Truby, aged 83, a resident of the Headington Union in Oxfordshire, sang four songs for Sharp on 12 and 13 September, 1923: *My Bonny Boy, The Sweet Primeroses, Green Bushes* and *Three Maids A-Milking*. This latter tune is the very last that Sharp transcribed into his fair copy manuscripts. There were no Trubys recorded at the Headington Union in the 1901 census.

Manuscript refs:
FT 4971-4973, 4977
FW none
Photo refs: none

THREE MAIDS A-MILKING

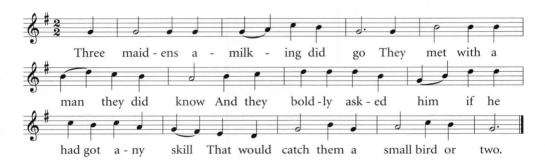

Three maid-ens a-milk-ing did go They met with a man they did know And they bold-ly ask-ed him if he had got a-ny skill That would catch them a small bird or two.

Three maidens a-milking did go
They met with a man they did know
And they boldly asked him if he had got any skill
That would catch them a small bird or two.

Second version from William Stokes

Three maidens a-milking did go
Three maidens a milking did go
The wind it did blow high, the wind it did
    blow low
And it waved their pails to and fro.

They met with some young man they knew
They met with some young man they knew
And they asked of him if he had any skill
In catching a small bird or two.

'O yes I have very good skill
O yes I have very good skill
O it's come along with me to the yonder
    green wood
And I'll catch you a small bird or two.'

Away to the green woods they went
Away to the green woods they went
And they tapped at the bush and the bird it
    did fly in
And it flew just above her lily-white knee.

Here's a health to the bird in the bush
Here's a health to the bird in the bush
For the birds of one feather they will all flock together
Let the people say little or much.

NOTES ON THE SONGS

Banks of Claudy sung by Mrs Slade at Minehead, Somerset, on 8 August 1904 (FT 272 / FW 378) Roud 266 / Laws N40.

One of the most popular of the 'broken token' songs, in which the lover returns in disguise, *Claudy Banks* was collected all over Britain and also in the USA, Canada, and Australia. It seems strange, therefore, that Sharp only noted one version in England.

Banks of Green Willow sung by Elizabeth Mogg at Holford, Somerset, on 30 August 1904 (FT 373 / FW 502) Roud 172 / Child 24. Sharp noted another eleven versions.

This song was very popular, and was collected many times in England. Child printed two Scottish versions from the early nineteenth century, but there is no evidence that it was much older than that. Despite numerous versions on which to draw, the basic story remains elusive. In some, it is the captain who throws the woman and baby overboard, in others it is the lover, in still others the woman throws herself, but the motive is not clear. Child proposed that this action was the result of casting lots when the ship was in danger, but this interpretation remains speculative. Nevertheless, there is sometimes the implication that she is thrown overboard to save the others on the ship.

Blackbirds and Thrushes sung by George Wyatt at W. Harptree, Somerset, on 15 April 1904 (FT 205 / FW 279) Roud 12657.

Sharp collected four other versions. None of these were textually complete, or even particularly coherent, and he therefore published a composite text in *Folk Songs from Somerset (Series Five)* (1909), pp. 10–12, but this has a slightly artificial feel to it. George Wyatt's version is much better in performance than in cold print, but the last line of verses 1 and 2 is more commonly sung as 'Jimmy will be slain in the wars, I'm afraid'.

The Blue Cockade sung by Susan Williams at Haselbury Plucknett, Somerset, on 2 September 1905 (FT 625 / FW 702-703)

Roud 191. Sharp noted another five versions.

Widely collected in England, and found on numerous broadsides, the colour of the cockade varies from singer to singer – white, blue, or green. Susan Williams' text lacks a verse which makes it clear that the curse with which the third verse commences is aimed at the recruiting sergeant, not at the lover.

Bonny Bunch of Roses sung by Tom Spracklan at Hambridge, Somerset, in September 1903 (FT 18 / FW 29-30) Roud 664 / Laws J5.

We have standardised 'O' and 'Oh' in the text. The text which Tom Spracklan sang omits some elements of the usual story, and we have therefore added one and a half verses (verse 3, and verse 4 lines 3 and 4) from a very similar version which Sharp noted from the singing of Capt. Lewis of Minehead in 1906.

Sharp obviously found this song interesting, as he noted it from 12 different singers.

One of the most popular of traditional songs, noted from singers all over Britain and Ireland, and printed on dozens of broadsides.

The Bonny Light Horseman sung by Jack Barnard at Bridgwater, Somerset, on 4 April 1908 (FT 1598 / FW 1449) Roud 1185.

Sharp also collected the song from William Russell of Eynsham, but again only two verses were noted. It was not possible to reconstruct the song by combining Jack Barnard's text with William Russell's, so we have provided both Barnard's words and a complete text from a Pitts broadside in the Madden Collection (London Printers (3) item 422).

The song was widely printed on broadsides, but not often noted from singers in England, and usually in shortened versions. These shorter versions often focus on the 'Broken-hearted I wander' lines.

Brimbledown Fair sung by Jim Woodland at Stocklinch, Somerset, on 8 April 1904 (FT 159 / FW 241) Roud 171.

Sharp noted three other versions, and he published a composite text in *Folk Songs from*

Somerset (Series Three) (1906). Even with these other versions, it was not possible to reconstruct the song without doing violence to each one, so we have supplied a fuller version collected by H. E. D. Hammond from William Barrett, Piddletown, Dorset, 1905 (D243).

Often called *Young Ramble Away,* this song was collected many times and also appeared on numerous nineteenth century broadsides. Versions vary considerably, and in some the young man's romantic wanderings are left in the abstract, but in others it is clear that he leaves Nancy pregnant and in sorrow.

Come All Brother Seamen sung by Jim Prole at Monksilver, Somerset, on 10 September 1906 (FT 1139) Roud 1638.

Sharp only collected the first verse from Jim Prole. The rest of the text is the whole version from Mrs Overd of Langport, Somerset, on 19 August 1904 (FT 327 / FW 453-454). Mrs Overd's text had a line missing in her verse 4, which was also missing in some broadside texts. We have supplied it from a Davenport broadside in the Madden Collection (Slip songs O-Y item 1786). This line introduces the word 'doxy', meaning in this context a prostitute or flash girl, but in others simply a girl, which is common in most other versions of the song. Also, in Mrs Overd's text, verse 4 line 2 and verse 6 line 3 we have substituted 'I' for 'he'.

This song was noted a few times by Sharp's contemporaries and successors in the field, and was also in the repertoires of well-known Norfolk singers Harry Cox and Walter Pardon. A mid-nineteenth century broadside version was entitled *The Tar's Frolic, or The Adventures of a British Sailor.*

Come Buy My Fine Herrings sung by Lucy White at Hambridge, Somerset, on 11 April 1904 (FT 166 / FW 254) Roud 12620.

This song does not seem to have been noted from anyone else, although Edith Fowke collected a similar song, *Silver Herrings,* from O. J. Abbott in Quebec in 1957. Similar songs existed (e.g. *Who'll buy my Sweet Lavender*), ostensibly based on street seller's cries, but these probably had an origin on the London stage.

The Dark-Eyed Sailor sung by William Nott at Meshaw, Devon, on 9 January 1904 (FT 96 / FW 161-162) Roud 265 / Laws N35.

Words in square brackets supplied by the editors to fill gaps in the MS. Sharp collected this song eight times. One of the most popular of folk songs, collected dozens of times across Britain and North America. Also very popular on broadsides from the 1820s onwards.

Death and the Lady sung by Mrs R. Sage at Chew Stoke, Somerset, on 11 January 1907 (FT 1161 / FW 1158) Roud 1031.

Sharp's manuscripts include another tune entitled *Death and the Lady,* noted from Sussex singer Thomas Burstow in 1908, who claims to have made it up himself. Sharp noted the song entirely in 5/4 time but his notation included 6 beats in some bars. We have noted these bars as 6/4 time.

Moral dialogues between Death and unfortunate mortals were extremely popular in songs and prints across Europe from the Middle Ages onwards. This particular treatment of the theme seems to date from the eighteenth century. For historical commentary, see William Chappell, *Popular Music of the Olden Time* (1859), pp. 164–8, and Lucy Broadwood, *English Traditional Songs & Carols* (1908), pp. 40-41, 118.

Dilly Song sung by Thomas Green at Wells Workhouse, Somerset, on 26 August 1908 (FT 1803) Roud 133.

Sharp collected another twelve versions in England, plus five more in the USA.

Under its most commonly recognised title of *Green Grow the Rushes O*, this is undoubtedly one of the most widely known traditional songs in Britain, thanks to its crossing over into 'community song' status. Consequently, since Sharp and his contemporaries first printed their collected versions, the song has been sung around countless camp-fires and during many a coach outing. The symbolism of the song has puzzled laypeople and scholars alike since late Victorian times, and it must take the prize for the folk song burdened with the largest quantity of nonsense written about it to explain its secret meaning. The song requires serious investigation.

Dream of Napoleon sung by William Durkin at Ilminster, Somerset, on 30 August 1905 (FT 610) Roud 1538.

Sharp only noted the first verse from William Durkin. The rest of the text is taken from a broadside entitled *The Nosegay*, containing eight songs, printed by Pitts of London, in the Madden Collection (London Printers (3) item 665a). Mr Durkin's verse is very similar to the broadside's first verse.

This was the only version Sharp noted, and although the song was collected from a few other singers in the twentieth century, it does not seem to have been as widely known as other Napoleon songs. It was, however, very popular on broadsides, with most of the leading printers including it in their catalogues. The earliest known printings probably date from the 1820s.

Farewell He sung by Lucy White and Louie Hooper at Hambridge, Somerset on 23 December 1903 (FT 65 / FW 88) Roud 803.

Sharp noted one other version. The chorus of the version printed here is from another song, very popular with traditional singers in America, called *I'll Be All Smiles Tonight*, written by T. B. Ransom in 1879. Sharp noted the song in the key of F, but we have transposed it to C for ease of singing.

Farewell Lads and Lasses Sung by Robert Parish at Exford, Somerset 20th Aug 1907 (FT 1420 / FW 1305) Roud 593.

These three verses are all that Sharp noted from Robert Parish, but the song is generally much longer. It was collected quite often in southern England, and also appears on nineteenth century broadsides. We have printed a longer version, for comparison, as collected by H. E. D. Hammond from Robert Barrett, in Dorset in September 1905.

The Foggy Dew sung by Lucy White and Louie Hooper at Hambridge, Somerset, on 23 December 1903 (FT 51 / FW 87) Roud 558 / Laws O3.

Sharp collected another seven versions in England, plus one in North America. An extremely widespread song, which has excited a great deal of scholarly interest, and several none-too-sensible theories about the meaning of the evocative phrase 'foggy dew'. The relatively prosaic truth is that in the earliest known broadside version of 1689, it is a 'bugaboo' or ghost which is manufactured by the young man to frighten the girl into his bed. See John Wardroper, *Lovers, Rakes and Rogues* (1995), pp. 87–88.

From Riches to Poverty sung by Mrs Lock at Muchelney Ham, Somerset, on 4 August 1904 (FT 257 / FW 362) Roud 1703.

Sharp found two other versions and it was only noted a handful of times by other collectors, although Baring-Gould claimed that he had come across it repeatedly in the West Country (*English Minstrelsie,* Vol. 6 (1896), pp. xi–xii). No known broadside versions.

The Gallant Huzzar sung by Emily Cockram at Meshaw, Devon, on 9 January 1904 (FT 92 / FW 153-154) Roud 1146.

We have retained the spelling of 'huzzar', as in the MS, as Sharp presumably deliberately wrote it this way to reflect the singer's pronunciation. He collected one other version.

This song was found often by collectors in Britain and North America in the twentieth century, in versions which differed little from each other. It was particularly popular with broadside printers, and nearly all the major printers included it in their catalogues from around the 1820s.

God Speed the Plough sung by William Cornelius at South Petherton, Somerset, on 10 April 1907 (FT 1347 / FW 1246) Roud 12762.

'God speed the plough' was a well-known phrase which featured in several nineteenth century songs, and was prominently displayed at Harvest Homes and printed on commemorative crockery. But we have not been able to locate another version of this particular song.

Ground for the Floor sung by Mrs Lock at Muchelney Ham, Somerset, on 4 August 1904 (FT 259 / FW 364-365) Roud 1269.

Mrs Lock could not remember the last four lines of her last verse, so we have added these from a Cambridgeshire version published in Lucy Broadwood's *English County Songs* (1893), pp. 96–97. This song on the pleasures of the simple life was collected a number of times in England, although this is the only version which Sharp noted. It was also regularly printed on broadsides, at least from the first decade of the nineteenth century onwards.

Here's to my Tin sung by Louie Hooper at Hambridge, Somerset, on 4 April 1904 (FT 133 / FW 208) Roud 475.

This was the only version of the song collected by Sharp, but it was regularly noted by other collectors in Britain, and particularly in Australia. The chorus varies considerably from version to version, including the well-known 'All for me grog', and 'Across the western ocean', and the theme of naming (and removing) clothes led to many bawdy treatments.

I Wish I had Never Known sung by Mrs Overd at Langport, Somerset, on 15 August 1904 (FT 297 / FW 401-402) Roud 1452.

Sharp also collected a version from Jane Gulliford of Combe Florey, Somerset. Only noted a handful of times in this form, although the sentiments, and many of the phrases, occur in a number of other songs.

The Irish Girl sung by William Brister at Ilminster, Somerset, on 30 August 1905 (FT 609) Roud 308.

Verse 1 line 3: in most versions this line ends with 'hair', which the rhyme seems to expect, but Sharp definitely wrote down 'eyes'. He only collected the first verse from William Brister, so we have supplied the full text he noted from Henry Corbet at Snowshill, Gloucestershire, on 9 April 1909 (FT 2154 / FW 2021).

Sharp noted six other versions.

This seemingly inconsequential song was immensely popular and collected in numerous versions across Britain, Ireland and North America during the twentieth century. It was also widely printed by the broadside presses, at least from around 1830 and probably earlier.

Jack the Jolly Tar sung by William Nott at Meshaw, Devon, on 12 January 1904 (FT 115 / FW 189-190) Roud 511 / Laws K40.

Verse 5 line 4: 'she came down' has replaced 'I came down'. Sharp noted two other versions.

This humorous variation on the Jack-on-shore theme was widely known in Britain and also collected regularly in North America. Given its popularity, it is surprisingly rare on extant broadsides, but the earliest known dates from about 1830.

John Barleycorn sung by Charles Neville at East Coker, Somerset, on 2 September 1908 (FT 1821) Roud 164.

Sharp noted only one verse from Charles Neville, so we have supplied the full text he collected from John Trump, North Petherton, Somerset, 18 April 1906 (FT 905 / FW 976). Sharp collected another fifteen versions.

A very widely known song in the twentieth century, which had lasted well in the tradition for over three hundred years. Our first evidence of its existence is on seventeenth century broadsides, and there is no reason to believe it any older. Certainly, there is no evidence beyond speculation that it has ancient origins or links with corn goddesses. One of the three seventeenth-century versions included in the Euing Collection of broadsides in Glasgow University, entitled *A Pleasant new Ballad to sing Evening and Morn, of the Bloody Murder of Sir John Barleycorn* takes thirty-four verses to tell the same story. Traditional singers very wisely sang relatively short versions.

King George sung by Mrs Overd at Langport, Somerset, on 22 December 1904 (FT 442 / FW 557) Roud 130. Sharp collected two other versions.

A widely known song, in North America as well as in Britain, more usually starting 'In Good King Arthur's time' or 'Good old Colony times'. There are two branches to the song, one which details the theft of cloth, as here, while the other focuses on food.

The Lake of Coul Fin sung by W. Smith at Marylebone Workhouse, London, on 25 September 1908 (FT 1934) Roud 189 / Laws Q33.

Sharp only collected the first verse from this singer. The second text is reproduced from Topic TSCD 653 (1998) *O'er His Grave the Grass Grows Green* (Voice of the People, Vol. 3), sung by Scan Tester, Sussex; recorded by Frank Purslow and Ken Stubbs (26 October 1960). Sharp noted seven other versions. Only the one from Mr Spearman of Ile Brewers, Somerset, included anything like a full text, and even his version omitted certain key points of the full story. Rather than combining several texts, we have decided to include the excellent version sung by Scan Tester.

Widely known in North America as well as Britain and Ireland, the only real differences from version to version tend to be the poor chap's name, and the spelling of the lakes. It has not been traced earlier than mid-nineteenth century broadside printings.

Long Tailed Blue sung by Mrs Susan Wilson at Shipham, Somerset, on 24 April 1906 (FT 936 / FW 994) Roud 1287.

Verse 2, line 1: the word 'niggers' has been replaced by 'people'.

Songs originating with blackface minstrel troupes were extremely popular all over Britain, but folk song collectors like Sharp tended to ignore them as being too recent for their tastes. *Long Tailed Blue* was also noted by Alfred Williams in Berkshire and Oxfordshire. Authorship was claimed by George Washington Dixon, who was singing it as early as 1827, and early sheet music versions can be seen in the Levy collection at http://levysheetmusic.mse.jhu.edu/

The Moon Shines Bright sung by James Beale at Warehorne, Kent, on 23 September 1908 (FT 1924 / FW 1779-1780) Roud 702. Sharp noted seven other versions.

This was a widely known song, popular with both Christmas carol and May Day singers, and it was regularly printed on annual carol broadsides from the late eighteenth century onwards.

Mummers' Song sung by John Thorne at Minehead, Somerset, 12 January 1906. (FT 769 / FW 827-828) Roud 13275.

In performance, most of the rough verse of a traditional mummers' play would have been declaimed with few embellishments. However, music also played a minor role in many versions. Mummers troupes often sang a song at the beginning of the performance, and in some instances this became a formal 'calling on' song which introduced the characters. Some plays had sung parts in the middle – especially the 'wooing plays' of Eastern England – and it was very common for troupes to entertain their audiences with songs after the play. The section of the Minehead text noted by Sharp as a song functioned as the finale to the play, although it reads as if it would have been better placed at the beginning.

New Year's Song sung by Frederick Crossman at Huish Episcopi, Somerset, on 5 January 1909 (FT 2032 / FW 1901) Roud 1066.

Crossman told Sharp that this song was 'Learned from "my old uncle". Always used to sing it at the church gate and when every one was enjoying themselves at Christmas. Also after ringing out the old year and ringing in the new, we used to go and sing it standing at the clergyman's door at Huish.' Verse 1 line 1: one would normally expect this line to end with 'beer', to preserve the rhyme scheme, but Sharp's MS clearly says 'cider'. Sharp noted one other version.

Songs involved in seasonal visiting customs by wassailers and mummers tend to take a relatively standard pattern across the country, wishing good health to the inhabitants and requesting money, food or drink for the visitors.

No My Love Not I sung by Lucy White at Hambridge, Somerset, on 13 April 1904 (FT 195 / FW 291) Roud 1403.

There are many songs about seduction, pregnancy and regret, and the text collected from Lucy White appears to combine two of them. As it stands, lines 1–8 and 17–20 are part of the song *No My Love Not I*, whereas 9–16 are more usually found in a similar song, *Down by the Riverside*, or *I Am Too Young* (Roud 564 / Laws P18), which Sharp also collected several times.

Second version: Sharp noted this other version of *No My Love Not I* from Mrs Overd at Langport, Somerset, on 22 August 1904 (FT 343 / FW 473). Mrs Overd's text also had two lines missing in verse 4. It was not easy to find words to insert here, as other versions were very different to Mrs Overd's at this point. The two lines are taken from a broadside text printed in Steve Gardham's *An East Riding Songster* (1982), p. 51.

O Once I was a Shepherd's Boy sung by Shepherd Hayden at Bampton, Oxfordshire, on 6 September 1909 (FT 2367) Roud 2407. This song seems to be unique to Shepherd Hayden.

On Christmas Time sung by William Bayliss at Buckland, Gloucestershire, on 6 April 1909 (FT 2131 / FW 2010) Roud 597.

No other versions in the Sharp manuscripts, but found in England by other twentieth century collectors. It featured regularly on annual Christmas carol sheets produced by broadside printers in the nineteenth century.

Once I Courted a Fair Young Woman sung by Frederick Crossman at Huish Episcopi, Somerset, on 29 July 1904 (FT 228 / FW 321) Roud 563 / Laws P12. Sharp noted one other version in England plus several in the USA, where it was widely known.

A version noted by an American sailor imprisoned in Portsmouth in 1778 is printed in George Carey, *A Sailor's Songbag* (1976), pp. 88–89.

Paddy Works on the Railway sung by John Short at Watchet, Somerset, on 21 April 1914 (FT 2894) Roud 208. No other versions in the Sharp manuscripts.

Widely reported in both Britain and North America, sometimes as a shanty but also as an ordinary song.

The Painful Plough sung by Thomas Mitchell at Merriott, Somerset, on 25 August

and 3 September 1905 (FT 599 / FW 689) Roud 355.

Sharp also collected this song from Job Francis of Shipley, Sussex in 1908 (FT 1664).

Collected many times in England and Scotland, and also popular on nineteenth century broadsides.

Poaching Song sung by Mrs Elizabeth Smitherd at Tewkesbury, Gloucestershire, on 10 April 1908 (FT 1627 / FW 1480) Roud 299.

Sharp collected two other versions of this song. More commonly known as the *Lincolnshire Poacher*, it is one of the best-known of English traditional songs, thanks to its inclusion in countless polite song books as well as on numerous broadsides. It was noted frequently by twentieth century folk song collectors. Its origin is still unclear, but the popular dramatist W. T. Moncrieff (1794–1857) claimed to have heard it sung at a public house and to have written new verses to the tune, and it is this version which proved of enduring popularity.

The Press Gang sung by Jack Barnard at Bridgwater, Somerset, on 4 April 1907 (FT 1310 / FW 1229-1230) Roud 601 / Laws N6. Sharp noted two other versions.

In short compass, and to great effect, this song includes several favourite folk song themes: cruel parents, sweetheart press-ganged, girl dressed as a sailor to follow him, recognition and happy ending.

The Pride of Kildare sung by William Briffett at Bridgwater, Somerset, on 17 August 1905 (FT 558 / FW 635-636) Roud 962 / Laws P6.

Verse 1 line 3: 'When I met' replaces 'when I meet'.

Sharp noted two other versions. A very popular song, often collected in England and North America, and also printed on numerous broadsides from at least the 1820s onwards.

Princess Royal sung by Capt. Vickery at Minehead, Somerset, on 9 August 1904 (FT 280) Roud 528 / Laws K29.

Sharp only noted the first verse from Capt.

Vickery, so we have provided the rest of the text as collected from Capt. Lewis at Minehead, Somerset (FW 389). Sharp collected five other versions.

This is one of the best known of all sea songs, noted all over Britain and in North America by twentieth century collectors. It was also printed on broadsides from about the 1820s, but not as often as one would expect from its popularity.

Queen Jane sung by Mrs Sweet at Somerton, Somerset, on 2 August 1906 (FT 959 / FW 1001 & 1086) Roud 77 / Child 170.

This was the only version of the song that Sharp collected in England, although he found others in the USA.

Jane Seymour, Henry VIII's queen, died twelve days after the birth of Prince Edward in 1537. However, popular rumour, turned into legend, presented a far more dramatic scenario of a baby being cut out of the womb at the mother's desperate request. This particular song has not been traced earlier than the 1770s, but another song on the same subject existed in the early sixteenth century.

Riggs o' London Town sung by Mrs Betsy Holland at Huntshaw Cross, Devon, 25 August 1907 (FT 1445 / FW 1328) Roud 868.

Verse 6 has only three lines in the manuscript, so we have added line 3 from a broadside text. Sharp collected two other versions.

Songs which feature the exploits of sailors or other visitors with 'flash girls of the city' were widely sung, turning up in many collectors' notebooks even though they could not publish the words without severe expurgation. This one was particularly popular and seems to have started life around the turn of the nineteenth century as *The Country Man's Ramble in Cheapside.*

The Sailor and the Soldier sung by William Stokes at Chew Stoke, Somerset, on 12 April 1909 (FT 2168 / FW 2032) Roud 350. Sharp collected one other version.

This popular song was found all over Britain in the early twentieth century, plus a few times in North America, but does not seem to have

featured on broadsides. Its format is ideal for extension and parody, and bawdy versions existed side by side with the more polite ones noted by the Edwardian collectors.

The Seeds of Love sung by John England at Hambridge, Somerset, on 22 August 1903 (FT 1 / FW 1) Roud 3. Sharp collected a total of 31 versions of this song.

Not only famous for being the first that Cecil Sharp noted down, this song was also extremely popular across Britain. As the musical historian William Chappell commented: 'If I were required to name three of the most popular songs among the servant-maids of the present generation, I should say, from my own experience, that they are *Cupid's Garden, I Sow'd the Seeds of Love,* and *Early One Morning*' (*Popular Music of the Olden Time* (1859), p. 735).

Still Growing sung by Harry Richards at Curry Rivel, Somerset, on 28 July 1904 (FT 233-234 / FW 315-316) Roud 31 / Laws O35.

Verse 4 line 6: 'O his grave was growing green' replaces 'O his grief was growing grief'. Sharp clearly thought highly of this song as he collected eleven other versions in England, plus one in the USA.

This is a widely known song, beloved by singers and collectors alike for its tragic/romantic story and good tunes. It was already known in the 1780s when Robert Burns remodelled it into his poem *Lady Mary Ann.*

Three Maids A-Milking sung by Mrs Truby at Headington Workhouse, Oxfordshire, on 13 September 1923 (FT 4977) Roud 290.

Sharp only noted one verse from Mrs Truby, so we also give the song as sung by William Stokes at Chew Stoke, Somerset, on 1 April 1907 (FT 1277 / FW 1207).

Sharp noted eight versions in addition to these.

This song was clearly a popular one and noted many times in England by other collectors, although it was not often published in an unedited form. It seems to have appeared on relatively few broadsides, but dates from at least the 1820s.

'Twas on an April Morning sung by Ellen Carter of Cheddar, Somerset, on 13 August 1908 (FT 1787) Roud 1546.

Sharp only collected one verse from Ellen Carter and no other version. We have supplied a text collected by L. Priscilla Wyatt-Edgell from Mr. R. Bryant at Cowley, Devon, in March 1908. This is published in *Journal of the Folk-Song Society*, 4 (1910), 94–96.

Although no other versions have been found, the notes in the *Journal* point out the song's affinity with the extremely widely known *Early One Morning*. This places it firmly in the context of pastoral laments for lost sweethearts, so popular on the eighteenth century stage.

Van Dieman's Land sung by Robert Parish of Exford, Somerset, on 6 September 1906 (FT 1126 / FW 1120) Roud 519 / Laws L18. Sharp noted two other versions in England.

Probably the best-known song on the theme of transportation, it was collected extensively in Britain and North America. Roy Palmer assigns the song's origin to about 1829/30, and argues that it was a response to draconian anti-poaching laws of the time (see *Folk Music Journal*, 3 (1976), 161–64).

We Serving Men Get Pleasure sung by Frederick Crossman at Langport, Somerset, on 23 January 1906 (FT 816 / FW 873) Roud 873. Sharp collected two other versions.

This is part of a much longer song, which reports a dialogue between a husbandman and a serving man concerning their respective merits. The version noted by Sharp from Henry Thomas runs to six eight-line verses. However, we think that Frederick Crossman's two verses make a perfectly respectable shorter song. Anyone interested in the longer Thomas version can find it transcribed in Maud Karpeles' *Cecil Sharp's Collection of English Folk Songs* (Vol. 2, pp. 211–12)

The Vicarage, Hambridge

CECIL SHARP AND FOLK SONG: A SELECT BIBLIOGRAPHY
Compiled by David Atkinson

Unpublished Cecil Sharp manuscripts and other materials

More detailed descriptions and information concerning the citation of the Cecil Sharp manuscripts can be found in 'The Citation of Unpublished Material by or Relating to Cecil Sharp', *Folk Music Journal*, 8 (2002), 132–35.

Cecil Sharp Manuscripts:
  Field Notebooks, Words (VWML)
  Field Notebooks, Tunes (VWML)
  Fair Copy Manuscripts, Folk Words (Clare College, Cambridge; copy at VWML)
  Fair Copy Manuscripts, Folk Tunes (Clare College, Cambridge; copy at VWML)
  Fair Copy Manuscripts, Folk Dance Notes (Clare College, Cambridge; copy at VWML)
  Index to Cecil Sharp Manuscripts (Clare College, Cambridge; copy at VWML)
  Correspondence (VWML)
  Miscellaneous Material (VWML)
Cecil Sharp Broadside Collection, 3 vols (VWML, accession nos. 1991, 2061, 2062)
Cecil Sharp Photograph Collection (VWML)
Cecil Sharp Press Cuttings (VWML)

Collections and writings of Cecil Sharp

The following is a simplified listing of Sharp's major publications on folk song – song books, contributions to the *Journal of the Folk-Song Society*, and critical writings – as well as some later selections edited by others. The publication history of Sharp's folk song collections is often complicated, and many publications are not clearly dated; some of them are described in more detail in Margaret Dean-Smith, *A Guide to English Folk Song Collections 1822–1952* (Liverpool: University Press of Liverpool in association with the English Folk Dance and Song Society, 1954). Individual songs collected by Cecil Sharp are catalogued in the VWML databases and in the Roud *Folk Song Index*.

Sharp made many additional contributions in the form of brief annotations in the *Journal of the Folk-Song Society* as well as arrangements of songs collected by others. This selection is based on items held in the VWML, with additional information from Dean-Smith and the catalogues of the VWML and the British Library.

Sharp, Cecil J., ed., *A Book of British Song for Home and School* (London: John Murray, 1902).

Sharp, Cecil J., and Charles L. Marson, eds, *Folk Songs from Somerset*, 5 series [4th and 5th Series ed. Cecil J. Sharp] (London: Simpkin, Marshall, Hamilton, Kent / Simpkin; Schott; Taunton: Barnicott and Pearce, 1904–09).

Sharp, Cecil J., 'Folk Songs Noted in Somerset and North Devon', *Journal of the Folk-Song Society*, 2 (1905), 1–60.

Baring Gould, S., and Cecil J. Sharp, *English Folk-Songs for Schools* (London: Curwen, [1906]).

Sharp, Cecil J., *English Folk-Song: Some Conclusions* (London: Simpkin; Novello; Taunton: Barnicott & Pearce, 1907); 2nd edn, Preface by Maud Karpeles (London: Novello; Simpkin Marshall; Taunton: Barnicotts, 1936); 3rd edn, revised by Maud Karpeles, with an appreciation of Cecil Sharp by Ralph Vaughan Williams (London: Methuen, 1954); 4th edn, revised by Maud Karpeles, with an appreciation of Cecil Sharp by Ralph Vaughan Williams (London: Mercury Books, 1965).

Sharp, Cecil J., ed., *Folk-Songs from Somerset*, Set I, Novello's School Songs, Book 201 (London: Novello, 1908).

Sharp, Cecil J., ed., *Folk-Songs from Somerset*, Set II, Novello's School Songs, Book 202 (London: Novello, 1908).

Sharp, Cecil J., 'Some Characteristics of English Folk-Music', *Folklore*, 19 (1908), 132–46.

Sharp, Cecil J., *Folk Songs (Various)*, Set III, Novello's School Songs, Book 212 (London: Novello, 1909).

Sharp, Cecil J., *Folk Songs (Various)*, Set IV, Novello's School Songs, Book 213 (London: Novello, 1909).

Gomme, Alice B., and Cecil J. Sharp, eds, *Children's Singing Games*, 5 sets, Novello's School Songs, Books 198–199, 227–229 (London: Novello, 1909–12).

Sharp, Cecil J., *Folk-Songs from Somerset*, Set V, Novello's School Songs, Book 222 (London: Novello, 1910).

Sharp, Cecil J., *English Folk-Carols, Collected in Various Parts of England* (London: Novello; Simpkin; Taunton: Barnicott and Pearce, 1911).

Sharp, Cecil, 'The Folk-Song Fallacy: A Reply', *English Review*, 11 (July 1912), pp. 542–50; rpt in *Folk Song Research*, 6 (1988), 48–56.

Sharp, Cecil J., *Folk-Songs from Various Counties*, Folk-Songs of England, Book IV (London: Novello, [1912]).

Sharp, Cecil J., *Folk Singing in Schools* (London: English Folk Dance Society, [1913]).

Sharp, Cecil J., *Folk-Song Carols*, Novello's School Songs, Book 245 (London: Novello, [1913]).

Sharp, Cecil J., *English Folk-Chanteys* (London: Simpkin, Marshall, Hamilton, Kent; Schott; Taunton: Barnicott & Pearce, 1914).

['Carols, Sailors' Chanties, Irish Songs, Ballads and Songs'], *Journal of the Folk-Song Society*, 5 (1914), 1–94.

Sharp, Cecil J., *Ballad Hunting in the Appalachians: Extracts of Letters Written by Cecil J. Sharp* (Boston: Todd [printer], 1916; rpt in Mike Yates, 'Cecil Sharp in America: Collecting in the Appalachians', *Musical Traditions*, Article MT052 http://www.mustrad.org.uk/articles/sharp.htm).

Sharp, Cecil J., ed. *One Hundred English Folksongs* (Boston: Oliver Ditson, 1916).

Sharp, Cecil J., 'Narrative and Historical Ballads and Songs', *Journal of the Folk-Song Society*, 5 (1916), 253–67.

Sharp, Cecil J., and Others, 'Songs of Country Life and Custom', *Journal of the Folk-Song Society*, 5 (1916), 268–76.

'Forfeit Songs; Cumulative Songs; Songs of Marvels and of Magical Animals', *Journal of the Folk-Song Society*, 5 (1916), 277–96.

Sharp, Cecil J., 'Sailors' Chanties', *Journal of the Folk-Song Society*, 5 (1916), 297–305.

Campbell, Olive Dame, and Cecil J. Sharp, *English Folk Songs from the Southern Appalachians* (New York and London: G. P. Putnam's Sons, 1917).

Sharp, Cecil J., and R. Vaughan Williams, *A Selection of Collected Folk-Songs*, Vol. I (London: Novello, [1917]).

Sharp, Cecil J., *Folk-Songs of English Origin Collected in the Appalachian Mountains*, 2 series (London: Novello, [1918–21]).

Sharp, Cecil J., *Ballads*, Novello's School Songs, Book 261 (London: Novello, [1919]).

Sharp, Cecil J., *English Folk Songs*, Selected Edition, 2 vols (London: Novello, [1920]; rpt in one vol., 1959).

Sharp, Cecil J., *Pulling Chanteys*, Novello's School Songs, Book 262 (London: Novello, n.d.).

Sharp, Cecil J., *Capstan Chanteys*, Novello's School Songs, Book 263 (London: Novello, n.d.).

Sharp, Cecil J., *Folk-Songs for Schools*, Set VII, Novello's School Songs, Book 268 (London: Novello, [1922]).

Sharp, Cecil J., *Folk-Songs for Schools*, Set IX, Novello's School Songs, Book 274 (London: Novello, [1925]).

['Narrative Ballads, Sea Songs, Love Songs, Sacred Songs and Carols, Miscellaneous Songs'], *Journal of the Folk-Song Society*, 8 (1927), 1–43.

Sharp, Cecil J., *English Folk Songs from the Southern Appalachians*, ed. Maud Karpeles, 2 vols (London: Oxford University Press, 1932).

Sharp, Cecil J., *Folk-Songs for Schools*, Set X, School Song Book 367 (London: Novello, [1936]).

Sharp, Cecil, *Twelve Songs for Children from the Appalachian Mountains*, piano accompaniments by Imogen Holst, 2 books (London: Oxford University Press, [1937]).

Sharp, Cecil J., *Sing Care Away, Book 4: Fifty-Eight English Folk Songs*, selected by Maud Karpeles (London: Novello, 1951).

Reeves, James, *The Idiom of the People: English Traditional Verse, Edited from the Manuscripts of Cecil J. Sharp* (London: Heinemann, 1958).

'Songs, Hitherto Unpublished, from the Manuscripts of Cecil Sharp', *Journal of the English Folk Dance and Song Society*, 8 (1959), 197–202.

Sharp, Cecil J., and Maud Karpeles, *Nine English Folk Songs from the Southern Appalachian Mountains*, piano accompaniments by Ralph Vaughan Williams (London: Oxford University Press, 1967).

Sharp, Cecil J., and Maud Karpeles, *Eighty English Folk Songs from the Southern Appalachians*, ed. Maud Karpeles, specimen piano accompaniments by Benjamin Britten, chord symbols by Pat Shaw (London: Faber and Faber in association with Faber Music, 1968).

Karpeles, Maud, ed., *Cecil Sharp's Collection of English Folk Songs*, 2 vols (London: Oxford University Press, 1974).

Karpeles, Maud, ed., *The Crystal Spring: English Folk Songs Collected by Cecil Sharp*, 2 vols (also in one vol.) (London: Oxford University Press, 1975).

Secondary sources

The following is a selective listing of writings relating to Cecil Sharp, his work on folk song, and the folk song revival at large.

Anderson, Hugh, 'Virtue in a Wilderness: Cecil Sharp's Australian Sojourn', *Folk Music Journal*, 6 (1994), 617–52.

Bearman, C. J., 'Cecil Sharp at Marlborough House: A Chapter of Biography', *English Dance & Song*, 60/2 (1998), 16–18.

Bearman, C. J., 'Who Were the Folk? The Demography of Cecil Sharp's Somerset Folk Singers', *Historical Journal*, 43 (2000), 751–75.

Bearman, Christopher James, 'The English Folk Music Movement 1898–1914', PhD thesis, University of Hull, 2001.

Bearman, C. J., 'Cecil Sharp in Somerset: Some Reflections on the Work of David Harker', *Folklore*, 113 (2002), 11–34.

Boyes, Georgina, *The Imagined Village: Culture, Ideology and the English Folk Revival*, Music and Society (Manchester: Manchester University Press, 1993).

Brockington, Allen, 'Cecil J. Sharp', *London Mercury*, 17, No. 102 (April 1928), 666–72.

Bronson, Bertrand H., 'Cecil Sharp and Folksong: A Review Article', *Western Folklore*, 27 (1968), 200–07.

Cox, Gordon, *A History of Music Education in England 1872–1928* (Aldershot: Scolar Press, 1993).

Dugaw, Dianne, 'Francis Child, Cecil Sharp, and the Legacy of the Pastoral in Folksong Study', *Folklore Historian*, 14 (1997), 7–12.

Etherington, Francis M., 'Cecil Sharp: Some Personal Reminiscences', *Journal of the English Folk Dance and Song Society*, 8 (1959), 194–96.

Fees, Craig, 'Cecil Sharp in Chipping Campden, Gloucestershire', *Folk Song Research*, 6 (1988), 58–61.

Fox Strangways, A. H., in collaboration with Maud Karpeles, *Cecil Sharp* (London: Oxford University Press, 1933).

Fox Strangways, A. H., and Maud Karpeles, *Cecil Sharp*, 2nd edn (London: Oxford University Press, 1955).

Frampton, George, 'In Search of Cecil Sharp: The Folk Song Society in Kent', *Bygone Kent*, 19/1 (1998), 7–13.

Francmanis, John, 'National Music to National Redeemer: The Consolidation of a "Folk Song" Construct in Edwardian England', *Popular Music*, 21 (2002), 1–25.

Gammon, Vic, 'Folk Song Collecting in Sussex and Surrey, 1843–1914', *History Workshop Journal*, no. 10 (1980), 61–89.

Harker, David, 'Cecil Sharp in Somerset: Some Conclusions', *Folk Music Journal*, 2 (1972), 220–40.

Harker, Dave, 'May Cecil Sharp Be Praised?', *History Workshop Journal*, no. 14 (1982), 44–62.

Harker, Dave, *Fakesong: The Manufacture of British 'Folksong' 1700 to the Present Day*, Popular Music in Britain (Milton Keynes: Open University Press, 1985).

Holst, Imogen, 'Cecil Sharp and the Music and Music-Making of the Twentieth Century', *Journal of the English Folk Dance and Song Society*, 8 (1959), 189–90.

Hughes, Meirion, and Robert Stradling, *The English Musical Renaissance 1840–1940: Constructing a National Music*, 2nd edn, Music and Society (Manchester:

Manchester University Press, 2001) [2nd edn of Robert Stradling and Meirion Hughes, *The English Musical Renaissance 1860–1940: Construction and Deconstruction* (London: Routledge, 1993)].

Karpeles, Maud, 'Cecil Sharp', *Journal of the English Folk Dance and Song Society*, 5 (1948), 139–41.

Karpeles, Maud, 'Cecil Sharp: Collector of English Folk Music', in *Studia Memoriae Belae Bartók Sacra* (Budapest: Akadémiai Kiadó, 1956), pp. 445–52.

Karpeles, Maud, 'Cecil Sharp: Collector and Restorer of English Folk Music', *Journal of the English Folk Dance and Song Society*, 8 (1959), 179–81.

Karpeles, Maud, *Cecil Sharp: His Life and Work* (London: Routledge & Kegan Paul, 1967).

Kennedy, Douglas, 'Cecil Sharp, the Teacher', *Journal of the English Folk Dance and Song Society*, 8 (1959), 186–88.

'Mr Cecil Sharp', *Musical Times*, 1 October 1912, pp. 639–43.

Newall, W. A., 'In the Footsteps of Cecil Sharp', *English Dance and Song*, 7 (1943), 26–27, 39–40.

Newman, Ernest, 'The Folk-Song Fallacy', *English Review*, 11 (May 1912), pp. 255–68; rpt in *Folk Song Research*, 6 (1987), 13–26.

Newman, Ernest, 'The Folk-Song Fallacy: A Rejoinder', *English Review*, 12 (August 1912), pp. 65–70; rpt in *Folk Song Research*, 6 (1988), 69–74.

Onderdonk, Julian, 'The Revised (1904) Version of the Folk Song Society's Hints to Collectors', *English Dance & Song*, 62/3 (2000), 21–23.

Palmer, Roy, 'Some Sharp Words', *English Dance & Song*, 55/2 (1993), 2–3.

Schofield, Derek, '1903 and All That', *English Dance & Song*, 56/1 (1994), 16–19.

Schofield, Derek, 'Sowing the Seeds: Cecil Sharp and Charles Marson in Somerset in 1903', *Folk Music Journal*, 8 (2004), forthcoming.

Sharp, Joan, 'Some Memories of Cecil Sharp', *Journal of the English Folk Dance and Song Society*, 8 (1959), 191–93.

Sykes, Richard, 'The Evolution of Englishness in the English Folksong Revival, 1890–1914', *Folk Music Journal*, 6 (1993), 446–90.

Wells, Evelyn K., 'Cecil Sharp in America', *Journal of the English Folk Dance and Song Society*, 8 (1959), 182–85.

Whisnant, David E., *All That Is Native & Fine: The Politics of Culture in an American Region*, The Fred W. Morrison Series in Southern Studies (Chapel Hill and London: University of North Carolina Press, 1983).

Wilgus, D. K., *Anglo-American Folksong Scholarship Since 1898* (New Brunswick, NJ: Rutgers University Press, 1959).

Wilson, Sir Steuart, 'Cecil Sharp: A Man of Zeal', *Musical Times*, 100 (Winter 1959), 584–85.

Yates, Michael, 'Percy Grainger and the Impact of the Phonograph', *Folk Music Journal*, 4 (1982), 265–75.

Yates, Mike, 'Cecil Sharp in America: Collecting in the Appalachians', *Musical Traditions*, Article MT052 http://www.mustrad.org.uk/articles/sharp.htm

Yates, Mike, 'Jumping to Conclusions', *Musical Traditions*, Enthusiasms no. 36 http://www.mustrad.org.uk/enthuse.htm

INDEX OF SONGS